ABOUT THIS BOOK
The objective of this guide is to give collectors the accurate market values of British coins in Great Britain, as sold by most dealers. For details of how condition affects prices, turn to p43.

Consultant Editor
Mark Rasmussen

Art Editor
Julie Bentley

Advertising Manager
Jay Jones

Advertising Production
Nik Harber

Illustrations supplied by
Mark Rasmussen

Chief Executive
Owen Davies

Published by
David Hall Publishing Ltd., Suite 6, Eden House, Enterprise Way, Edenbridge, Kent, TN8 6HF
ISBN 978 1 916159 1 2

Distributed to the news trade by:
Seymour Distribution Ltd, 2 East Poultry Avenue, London EC1A 9PT.

Distributed to the book trade by:
Booksource, 50 Cambuslang Rd, Cambuslang, Glasgow G32 8NB

Printed by
William Gibbons & Sons Ltd, 26 Planetary Road, Willenhall, West Midlands WV13 3XT.

Every care has been taken in compiling this guide: the publishers do not accept any responsibility for errors and omissions and their consequences.

CONTI

ABOVE: A Henry VIII Posthumous Sovereign, Bristol Castle, from the Horace Hird collection, sold by Spink for £67,200

LATEST MARKET PRICES

Mark Rasmussen Numismatist

Specialising in Coins of Great Britain, Scotland, Ireland and the Islands

A small selection of notable coins handled in recent years

Twenty Pound Piece
of James VI of Scotland

Sovereign of Henry VII

Sovereign of Henry VIII

Ryal of Elizabeth I

Triple Unite of Charles I

Five Guineas of Charles II

Countermarked U.S. Dollar of George III

Proof Gold Penny of George III

1933 Penny of George V

1935 Proof Crown in Gold

1937 Penny of Edward VIII

1819 Sovereign of George III

1952 Penny of George VI

1937 Threepence of Edward VIII

P. O. Box 42, Betchworth, Surrey RH3 7YR
Telephone/Fax: 01306 884 880
Mobile: 07798 611006
e-mail: mark.rasmussen@rascoins.com   www.rascoins.com

THE YEAR IN COINS

Discover the biggest sellers at auction in the last 12 months and the latest state of the British coin market

The review this year will cover the numismatic market post covid. However, while writing this review, the Ukraine war has been ongoing for six weeks with the potential to last much longer. While the impact of covid has receded, the war in Ukraine has carried forward economic uncertainty in the world. In addition, it is expected most major economies will enter into recession in the second half of 2022 continuing into 2023. Inflation has significantly increased globally along with the price of oil and gas. These events will shape prices and demand for the foreseeable future. With this in mind the price of gold, which had dipped, has since surged ahead and is currently over £1,495 per ounce.

With freedom of movement coming back in most of the world, normality is returning. Coin fairs have restarted and reported high levels of attendance. The yearly BNTA show in London was also busy, and many international dealers showed up. With fairs reopening, collectors can once again return to buying direct from dealers. During the various lockdowns, auctions had experienced a record number of bidders – mostly from clients at home in lockdown. This pattern is now expected to change with events recommencing.

Demand remains strong as usual for the finest pieces. The 'Hird' collection, sold by Spink on 28 September 2021, realised some eye wateringly high prices, with some items fetching many times their estimate. Swiss auction company Sincona offered part one of an English gold collection. This sale contained some exceptional rarities. All coins were reserved very low so it came as no surprise when the realised prices were far greater than expected. Mark Rasmussen produced a superb fixed price list which included exceptional early gold, plus an outstanding collection of sovereigns formed by a private collector over many years. The list also included the 'Dexter' collection of Crowns. The coins were all sold very quickly as the demand for sovereigns, early gold and crowns continues to outstrip supply.

Other interesting events during the pandemic were the entry to market of speculative investors, and an unprecedented surge in prices for modern issues occurred. These commemorative coins were mostly minted by the Royal Mint from 2019. These limited editions, commemorating engravers, pop stars etc, increased in price very quickly with trading on various platforms. However, these investors seem to be exiting the market as prices for the same coins are decreasing. There was another notable surge from dealers and collectors buying coins which have been encapsulated and graded by US companies. These third party grading companies grade everything from Celtic staters to modern issues. There's been much discussion at the range of grades on various types with many disagreeing on the outcome. There's much to be said for holding a coin in your hand to examine it, rather than looking through a plastic holder. However, the demand for third party graded coins remains strong so this new market is set to continue.

Through the pandemic collectors have been buying, selling and trading their collections. As collectors have had more time to pursue hobbies, more trading was noticeable, and all areas of the market had surges of new interest. This increased collector/investor interest saw higher prices being achieved in the last year in all levels of numismatics from lower grade examples to the finest known. It's possible that a levelling off will happen, and pricing stability will occur. Some normality could then return to the market, which can only be a good thing.

As always it's great to support your regular dealers as it is their income, and it's been a tough few years for most of them. So as things reopen, show your support at shows, fairs and events. Looking ahead we expect that future reviews will have more dealers lists to discuss rather than the vast number of coin auctions currently ongoing.

One thing we can all learn from the pandemic is that coin collectors remained loyal to their hobby. The interest in numismatics, the history and beauty of these small pieces of art, captures the imagination of generations of collectors, and will contunue to do so for the forseeable future.

ABOVE: Chris Rudd sold a rare Sego Warrior gold stater for £9,600 (image not shown actual size)

CELTIC COINAGE

There has been an absence of major collections coming to the market in the last year, but Chris Rudd continues to offer fresh material in his regular auctions. Auction 182 in May 2022, had a Belgae, Petal Saltire, gold quarter stater on offer, which realised £5,280 and had an estimate of £4,000. Auction 183 in July 2022, sold some rarities, including an attractive Sego Warrior stater, sold at the estimate price of £9,600. This is a good price for such a rare coin, as it's thought there are only three in private hands. A remarkable Iceni, Bury Diadem, Solar Anemone type, silver unit, sold for £6,600, against an estimate of £1,500. This exceedingly rare and highly artistic coin is an amazing survivor, as the smaller denominations do not survive the ravages of time unlike the gold coins.

ABOVE: Chris Rudd sold a rare Iceni, Bury Diadem. This Solar Anemone type, silver unit, sold for £6,600 (image not shown actual size)

HAMMERED GOLD

It has been an exciting year for hammered gold with some great rarities coming on the market. Hammered gold has always been extremely popular with collectors globally. As usual, prices for rarities and high-grade pieces remain very strong. Hammered gold encompasses a wide range of history from Celtic staters through to the triple unites of Charles I, and it's still possible to buy smaller or lesser-grade pieces for the low hundreds of pounds.

Spink sold a Henry III gold penny of twenty pence for £648,000 in January 2022. This coin was found on the 26 September 2021 by a detectorist in the village of Hemyock, Devon. The detectorist not knowing what he had found put images on social media where its importance was uncovered. This great rarity is one of eight known examples. It was struck by the king's goldsmith William Fitzotto of Gloucester. The coin shows Henry III enthroned on the Great Pavement in

ABOVE: Spink sold a Henry III gold penny of twenty pence, in January 2022, for a record £648,000

Westminster Abbey. The coin's value is twenty pence and struck in gold, and is twice the weight of a silver penny of the era. It is the highest value detector find to date, also a great addition to our history. What an exciting find, and also a life-changing amount for the detectorist.

Another great rarity was sold in 2022. The coin in question was a gold Leopard of Edward III, third coinage, minted in around 1343. At the time the coin proved unpopular with the public and was recalled and subsequently replaced with the noble seven years later. There are only five known examples with most in museums. This example was found in 2019 in Reepham, North Norfolk. It was folded in half when found, and subsequently repaired and sold at auction. It was sold by DNW for £173,600 against a pre-sale estimate of £100–140,000.

St James's auctions sold part two of the Comber collection. The finest collection of Elizabeth I coins ever formed. This superbly catalogued sale once again was full of Elizabethan treasures. Some of the many highlights was a beautiful Sovereign, sixth issue, mint mark A (1583–85). The sovereign was described as a 'superb example, extremely fine', ex Christie's 1962. It sold for £103,200 against a pre-sale estimate of £30–40,000. Another beautiful example was a gold half pound, sixth issue, mint mark tun (1593–94). This example was described as 'good extremely fine', and realised £36,000 against a pre-sale estimate of £15–20,000. Once again showing the demand for top quality remains strong.

Spink offered the 'Hird' collection of hammered gold on the 28 September 2021. Horace Hird had been a serious collector in the mid 1900's, assembling some great rarities. Although a lot of the collection had been sold in 1961, this part remained intact and was extensively catalogued by Spink. The group offered were fresh to the market having been unavailable for

HAMMERED SILVER

Once again prices have overall increased in hammered silver. The historic context of many of these issues increases interest from a collecting point of view. Collectors of mints can form quite a collection just from the various issues during the reign of Charles I. These pieces are not just provincial issues, they encompass all the coins issued in the English civil war between 1642–49. Some pieces are exceptionally rare such as Carlisle siege pieces (October 1644–June 1645). An example of a Carlisle shilling sold at Spink on 23 January 2022 for £20,400 against an estimate of £15–20,000. The most exceptional rarities are the Scarborough issues minted between July 1644–July 1645. Collectors of these issues can really add the historical context to the coins in their collections.

decades. There were some great rarities in this sale, and the coins were keenly fought over and realised high prices. Highlights included a Henry VIII posthumous issue Sovereign of Bristol, a great rarity, believed to be only two known and not represented in many of the famous collections, and seemed a bargain at £67,200. There was also an extremely rare Elizabeth I pattern twopence struck in gold, which realised £576,000, against an estimate of £10–15,000. An exceptional James I spur ryal, also made an appearance, second coinage (1611–12), with a mullet privy mark, in beautiful condition. This is a great rarity, with three recorded specimens, and has a wonderful pedigree. It realised a staggering £312,000.

On 21 November 2021 DNW offered the George Holloway collection of Elizabeth I Sovereigns – solely first and second issue coins. To find a single example of one of these issues is rare, but to have a whole sale of 33 lots devoted to them is exceptional. It was the collecting life of Mr Holloway, who had written a number of articles, he also left an archive detailing the 341 specimens he had inspected. The realised prices were strong and there was plenty of bidding activity. The first lot was a first issue Sovereign, mint mark lis (1559–60), described as 'extremely fine, practically as struck'. There are only eight known examples with this mint mark, so it's very rare. This choice example sold for £173,600 against a pre–sale estimate of £60–80,000.

Other areas of hammered silver are Anglo Saxon. These issues can often be crudely struck and extremely rare. These pieces are becoming very sought after, subsequently when collections appear on the market they are sold at some speed as demand is strong. This occurred when Canterbury auctions offered a collection formed over many years by an academic numismatist, John Cross.

Canterbury auctions sold the John Cross collection of Anglo Saxon coins on the 3 October 2021. John Cross was a noted authority and collector, so it was not a surprise that the collection was full of great rarities. Included in the collection offered was an extremely rare Ecbert (780 AD) silver penny, which realised £5,760 against an estimate of £250–300. Another coin of note was an excellent example of a silver penny of Coelnoth, Archbishop of Canterbury (833–70) which sold for £6,000 against a pre–sale estimate of £1–1,500. Although Anglo Saxon gold is very rare, the sale did include a Gold Thrymsa (644–660) Northumbria/York, that sold for £21,000.

Spink sold the Jean–Marie Vanmeerback collection of numismatic portraits on the 23 January 2022. This outstanding collection had been formed over many years. One of the highlights was a Henry VIII Testoon – one of the best examples displaying the characteristic Holbein image. This coin came with a very good provenance – the J. P. Storer and M. Hughes collections. It was sold for £50,400, well over double estimate – a bold price for a coin of this type. In the same sale was

an attractive Philip and Mary shilling (1553–4), described as 'approaching extremely fine'. This desirable coin sold for £102,200.

ABOVE: Mark Rasmussen, List 36, sold an extremely fine Charles II 1675, two guineas, for £39,500

ABOVE: Spink sold a superb portrait Henry VIII Testoon from the Vanmeerbeeck collection for £50,400

MILLED GOLD
Once again milled gold performed strongly in the last year. Most of the high value pieces seem to be going abroad as collectors in the US and Japan have very deep pockets. In addition, most higher-grade coins that are sold in the UK appear soon after in US auctions, normally encapsulated in plastic. It seems no matter how much material appears on the market it is swallowed up by collectors and investors. Five guinea's and Una and the Lion five-pound pieces have stabilised after years of incredible increases. However, proof and pattern issues have jumped in price with the finest commanding top prices.

Mark Rasmussen issued his fixed price list number 35 in the summer of 2021 and included a selection of early gold including a James I Sovereign of Twenty shillings, first coinage. This coin was described as 'practically as struck and extremely rare', listed at £42,500, and not surprisingly – it sold. A delightful Charles II 1675, two guineas, with reflective fields, sold for £39,500. Also in this list was 'The Bletchley collections of Sovereigns' collection, formed over many years and one of the finest to come on the market, highlights included an extremely rare 1819 Sovereign, described as Fair, listed for £25,000. There was also a 1830 Pattern by Wyon, extremely rare, for sale at £25,000, and one of the finest 1841 Sovereigns was listed at £25,000. An outstanding 1887 Sydney Mint Proof by Boehm, was described as exceedingly rare, ex Murdoch, and listed at £65,000.

Heritage auctions provided some tasty offerings in their 10 January 2022 sale. All coins sold by Heritage are encapsulated and graded by third party companies. Highlights of this sale included a choice 1656 Oliver Cromwell gold Broad of twenty shillings. This example was graded as MS63, it sold for $108,000 (USD). A superb 1726 George I two guineas, graded as MS65 sold for $66,000 and a beautiful 1693 William and Mary two guineas, graded as MS63, sold for $52,800. A 1741/38 five guineas, graded MS63, sold for $156,000.

Over the last two years modern issues have seen an exponential growth in prices. The prices had increased dramatically soon after the coins were issued. This market was assumed to be speculative with investors buying and selling these issues. The coins could be seen being bought and sold on various trading platforms. It can be assumed that this market is connected to the pandemic, investors entered and exited with some speed. The market for modern issues has never seen such activity, and many of the coins were sold to Japanese buyers. However, as we exit the pandemic we can see that the heady prices for these coins are coming down and correcting themselves. As interest rates increase, it can be assumed these speculative investors will exit the market for these issues.

MILLED SILVER
One of the most popular series in numismatics is milled silver. It covers monarchs from Charles II to Elizabeth II. Collectors can choose to collect monarchs or even houses, from Stuart to Windsor. Silver has always been the most minted of coins, and can therefore be the most affordable, depending of course on grade and rarity. Victorian coins are extremely popular, and there are some beautifully engraved coins. One of the most desired is the 1847

Gothic Crown. These coins have seen a renewed interest with prices jumping for finer examples. It is easy to see why they are so popular, the engraving by William Wyon is quite exceptional and beautiful, exemplifying the Gothic period. William Wyon was chief engraver at the Royal Mint until 1851, his work is some of the finest in numismatics.

Heritage auctions sale on the 10 January 2022 had some excellent silver coins, and highlights included a 1724 Shilling, WCC below bust, mined from silver from the 'Welsh Copper Company'.

ABOVE: In their January 2022 sale, Heritage sold an extremely rare 1699 proof shilling, ex. Manville collection, for $16,800

This example had an excellent provenance, ex Manville collection, it was graded as AU58, and sold for $31,200. Other rarities included an extremely rare 1699 Proof Shilling, graded as PF63 – again ex Manville collection – which sold for $16,800. However, the surprise price was for an 1847 Gothic Crown, struck in fine silver and plain edge, graded PF63, which sold for $132,000.

In Mark Rasmussen's fixed price list of summer 2021 he offered the 'Dexter' collection of Crowns. In this collection was a Charles I Exeter mint example, described as 'a superb example, practically as struck' offered at £4,850. It sold to a private client who will enjoy owning such a fine example. Another highlight was a 1662 Crown, described as practically extremely fine. This coin has an excellent provenance, ex Van Roekel and Dr Rees–Jones collections and was offered at £8,250. A high grade 1723 issue, described at extremely fine was offered at £6,500. In the same list there was an exceptional 1743 Crown, described at 'practically as struck' extremely fine, which was offered at £4,875. Demand for milled silver was strong and the collection sold fast.

COPPER AND BRONZE

This area continues to be popular with collectors, and it is also affordable. There are many rarities and date runs that can be collected. There are dealers who are specialists in bronze and copper – farthings in particular. Collectors can build quite a collection without spending too much money.

SCOTTISH

Demand for Scottish coinage is steady, no major collections have been sold in the last year, but St James's auction 62, The Christopher Comber Collection part III, offered a rare group of six shillings. These are very rare coins in any condition; a James VI 1605 example, possibly the finest known, described as good very fine, sold mid–estimate for £4,320 and is the plate coin in Spink's Standard Catalogue. A Charles I 1633, a very fine specimen realised £2,160.

ABOVE: St. James's, Comber part III, sold a superb James VI 1605, six shillings, for £4,320

IRELAND

Irish coins remain popular with DNW (now Noonans) selling The Michael Gietzelt collection of British and Irish coins, in their September 2021 sale. A Cities of Refuge, Cork, shilling, 1647 was hammered down for £12,400. St James's auction 48, The Christopher Comber Collection part II, 2021. had 29 pieces of Henry VIII Harp coinage, being the subject of his lecture entitled "The Irish Harp Coinage of Henry VIII, The Definitive Version". A first issue halfgroat, sold for £22,500 against an estimate of £5,000 and this whole series was strongly contested, witnessed by the high realised prices. An Edward VI, threehalfpence, posthumous issue in the name of Henry VIII fetched over four times estimate at £6,240. A Mary shilling, with a 'superb' portrait sold for £11,520 nearly double the high estimate, and an Elizabeth I, fine coinage,

ABOVE: Part II of the Comber collection, sold by St James's, included the only known Henry VIII and Jane Seymour Irish 'harp' half groat, it realised £22,500 (image not shown actual size)

1561 sixpence, practically as struck, made £3,360. Elusive pieces in high grade, remain highly sought after, and when they appear in auction, records are being broken.

ANGLO GALLIC

This series is supported by an elite group of collectors in the UK and on the continent, although there has been little to report in the last year, but this market remains strong.

THE ISLANDS

Isle of Man coins seem to be the most popular amongst collectors and the coins realise strong prices, Jersey and Guernsey seem less popular and appear somewhat underrated. The Michael Gietzelt Collection of Coins, Tokens and Medals of the Isle of Man and the Channel Islands, was sold by DNW (Noonans) in April 2022. A James Stanley Pattern penny, 1723 realised £7,440 against a low estimate of £4,000 another example a pattern of 1732 sold for £3,970.

TIPS FOR COLLECTING

If you are new to the hobby, here is some advice to get you started and put you in touch with the experts

HOW MUCH IS IT WORTH?

There was a time when newcomers to coin collecting would ask "What is it?" Nowadays, the most common question dealers hear is "What is it worth?"

British Coins Market Values aims to place a value on all the coins in the British Isles, in other words England, Wales, Scotland, Ireland and the Channel Islands as well as the Anglo–Gallic series and British banknotes.

This is a difficult task because many items don't turn up in auctions or lists every year, even though they are not really rare. However, we can estimate a figure so you have an idea of what you will have to pay.

HOW TO SELL AT AUCTION

Potential sellers have considerable choice when it comes to auction houses. In London alone, there are several: Spink & Son Ltd, St James's, Baldwins, Sovereign Rarities, (Dix Noonan Webb) now known as Noonans, Morton & Eden and London Coins. There are also smaller companies up and down the country, such as Corbetts of Newcastle and Croydon Coin Auctions.

The best approach for the seller is to compare the auction houses' catalogues and to attend the auctions so that you can see how well they are conducted.

Talk over your collection with the specialist, as you may find that one of the firms will look after your needs better than the others.

A well–known coin requires little expertise and will probably sell at a certain price in most auctions. However, if you require cataloguing of a specialist collection of a more academic nature, for example early Medieval coinages, then you need to know what a company is capable of before you discuss a job rate.

Remember that, while it is not complicated to sell by auction, and a good auction house will guide you through the process, you may have to wait three or four months from the time you consign the coins to the auctioneers before you receive any money.

There are times when items at auction manage to achieve very high prices, and other times when, for some reason, they fail to reach even a modest reserve.

Finally, auctioneers will usually charge you at least 10% of the knock–down price, and will charge the buyer a premium of up to 22.5% plus VAT.

HOW TO TRADE WITH DEALERS

The British coin market is very much dependent upon and benefits from the support of a strong network of dealers, with their professional numismatic expertise and long experience of the business. Fortunately, the needs of the collector, at any level, are eminently well served by them.

Most offer a large and varied stock of coins for sale at marked prices. And all dealers will provide advice and guidance on any aspect of collecting or disposal free of charge. When selling to a dealer, it is true that they generally prefer to obtain fresh material.

A proportion of dealers also offer to sell on a commission basis. In this instance the retail prices would be discussed in advance, allowing the collector a degree of control and a far more active role in the dispersal of their collection. Accordingly, the dealer offers a valuable and unique personal service and it is this relationship which has been responsible for helping to form some of our greatest numismatic collections.

BULLION COINS

Bullion coins can be priced simply by looking at the price of gold, which is fixed twice daily by a group of leading banks. Most newspapers carry this information in their financial pages.

Anyone can buy bullion coins (investment gold), such as sovereigns or Krugerrands, and they are not subject to VAT.

Normally, when you sell a bullion coin you should expect the coin dealer to make a few pounds profit on each coin. For mounted or damaged coins do not expect more than their intrinsic value.

HOW TO COLLECT COINS

You should obviously purchase your coins from a reputable dealer or auction house.

You can be sure of some protection if you choose a member of the British Numismatic Trade Association or the International Association of Professional Numismatists.

Membership lists, detailing dealers' main interests, can be obtained from the respective secretaries:

■ Christel Swan, 3 Unwin Mansions, Queen's Club Gardens, London W14 9TH. Tel: 07799 662 181. Email: secretary@bnta.net. Website: www.bnta.net

■ Jean-Luc Van Der Schueren, 14 Rue de la Bourse, B 1000 Brussels, Belgium. Tel: +32 2 513 3400. www.iapn-coins.org

However, many are not members of either organisation, but it does not mean that they are not honest and professional. The best approach is to find one who will unconditionally guarantee that the coins you buy from him are genuine and accurately graded.

You should buy coins in the best condition available, which is normally considered to be Extremely Fine or better. This applies particularly to the milled (post-1600) series, which is more commercial and therefore has a bigger emphasis on condition.

Hammered coins should be clear, legible and struck in good metal, with Very Fine being perfectly acceptable. One can obtain specimens in higher grade but they are much more difficult to get than their milled counterparts.

Collectors should be prepared that in some series and in the case of great rarities, they might have to make do with a coin that is only Fine or even Poor. It depends on factors such as type, reign and rarity and of course affordability, so try to be realistic.

It is worth taking out subscriptions with auction houses so that you regularly receive their catalogues, because this is an excellent way to keep up with current market prices and trends, as well as the collections that are being offered. Arguably, just as important are dealers' fixed price lists, where coins can be chosen and purchased at leisure by mail order or alternatively from the internet.

A good cross-section of other dealers, who produce excellent retail lists, either for mail order or online, in alphabetical order, follows:

■ A H Baldwin & Sons, 399 Strand, London, WC2R 0LX. Hammered and milled.

■ AMR Coins, PO Box 352, Leeds, LS19 9GG. Hammered and milled.

■ ASPREY COINS Langstone Park , Langstone Rd. Havant, Hampshire PO9 1SA

■ Lloyd Bennett, PO Box 2, Monmouth, Gwent NP25 3YR. Hammered, milled, tokens.

JULY 2022

■ Classical Numismatics Group (Seaby Coins), 20 Bloomsbury Street, London, WC1B 3QA. Hammered, some milled.

■ Coinage of England, 11, 1 Sloane Court East, Chelsea, SW3 4TQ.

■ Dorset Coin Company, 193 Ashley Road, Parkstone, Poole, Dorset BH14 9DL. All coins and banknotes.

■ K B Coins, PO Box 499, Stevenage, Hertfordshire, SG1 9JT. Hammered, milled.

■ Timothy Millet, PO Box 20851, London SE22 0YN. Medallions.

■ Simon Monks, PO Box 299, Lowestoft. NR32 9GD. Medallions, tokens, hammered, milled.

■ Peter Morris, PO Box 223, Bromley, Kent BR1 4EQ. Hammered, milled, tokens.

■ Mark Rasmussen, PO Box 42, Betchworth, Surrey RH3 7YR. Hammered, milled, medallions, tokens.

■ Roderick Richardson, The Old Granary Antiques Centre, King's Staithe Lane, King's Lynn, Norfolk PE30 1LZ. Hammered and milled.

■ Chris Rudd, PO Box 222, Aylsham, Norfolk NR11 6TY. Celtic.

■ Simmons Gallery, PO Box 104, Leytonstone, London E11 1ND. Medallions, tokens.

■ Sovereign Rarities Ltd, 32, St. George Street, Mayfair, London, W1S 2EA. Greek, Roman and Byzantine periods, British and World coins, Indian and Islamic coins, commemorative medals, and numismatic books.

■ Studio Coins, 1, Studio 111, 80, High Street, Winchester, Hampshire, SO23 9AT. Hammered.

■ Mike Vosper, PO Box 32, Hockwold, Brandon IP26 4HX. Ancient, Celtic, hammered.

SOCIETIES

Consider joining your local numismatic society, of which there are over 50 across the UK. To find if there is one near you, get in touch with the present Secretary of the British Association of Numismatic Societies (BANS), William Pugsley, 0777 1764 200. Email: bill.pugsley@pugsley.bz

BANS organises annual congresses and seminars, and it is a good idea for the serious collector to consider attending these. Details are published in the numismatic press or available via their website.

Collectors who wish to go further can apply for membership of the British Numismatic Society. The Society holds ten meetings each year at the Warburg Institute, Woburn Square, London, WC1H 0AB, in addition to out-of-town lecture days. As a member, you receive a copy of the *British Numismatic Journal*, which has details of current research, articles and book reviews.

The current Secretary of the Society is Peter Preston-Morley, c/o The Warburg Institute, Woburn Square, London, WC1H 0AB. Email: secretary@britnumsoc.org

COIN FAIRS

It's important to see coins in museums, but remember there's also a fine array at coin fairs. Most dealers don't mind showing coins to would-be collectors, even if they can't afford to buy them on the spot.

The UK's premier international numismatic show, the BNTA Coinex show, is held in late September every year. For more information call the BNTA Secretary, Christel Swan, Tel: 07799 662 181. Email: secretary@bnta.net. Website: www.bnta.net

Mike and Lu Veissid run the London Coin Fairs at the Holiday Inn, Bloomsbury, London on the first Saturday in February, June September and November. For all enquiries contact Lu Veissid. Tel: 01694 731781. Email: l.veissid@btinternet.com

The Bloomsbury Coin Fair is held seven times a year at the Royal National Hotel, 38–52, Bedford Way, London, WC1H 0DG. Contact John & Sophie Philpotts. Tel: 01242 898107. Email: bloomsburycoinfair.com. Website: info.bloomsburycoinfair.com

The monthly Midland Coin Fair, is on the second Sunday of every month at the National Motorcycle Museum in Birmingham. For further details, contact Lu Veissid. Tel: 01694 731781 or visit: www.coinfairs.co.uk. Email: l.veissid@btinternet.com

For the Harrogate Coin Show, Old Swan Hotel, Harrogate, in April, contact John & Sophie Philpotts. Tel: 01242 898107. Email: info@harrogatecoinfair.com

There are also biannual coin and stamp fairs at York racecourse in January and July. These are coordinated by Kate Puleston and Chris Rainey. Tel: 01425 656459 or 0208 946 4489. Or visit: www.stampshows.net

STORING YOUR COINS

Here are some helpful hints, along with some of the best accessories on the market, to help you keep your collection in good condition

ABOVE: One of Peter Nichols' handmade wooden cabinets

S tore coins carefully, as a collection which is carelessly or inadequately housed can suffer irreparable damage.

Water vapour causes corrosion and therefore coins should not be stored in damp attics or spare bedrooms but, where possible, in evenly-heated warm rooms.

One must be careful only to pick up coins by the edges, as sweaty fingerprints contain corrosive salt.

WOODEN CABINETS

A collection carefully laid out in a wooden cabinet looks very impressive.

Unfortunately, custom-built wooden cabinets are not cheap.

Their main advantages are the choice of tray and hole sizes but also, more importantly, they are manufactured from untreated well-matured wood, ideally mahogany, which has historically proven to be the perfect material for the long-term storage of coins.

Peter Nichols' handmade mahogany coin and medal cabinets can be made to order.
Tel: 0115 922 4149. www.coincabinets.com

Cabinets are also manufactured by Rob Davis in Ticknall, Derbyshire. Tel: 01332 862755. www.robdaviscoincabinets.co.uk

If you cannot afford a new cabinet, then a second-hand one may be the answer.

These can sometimes be purchased at coin auctions

ABOVE: Attaché cases are available from the Duncannon Partnership

or from dealers but it can be hard to find one with tray hole sizes to suit your coins.

Do-it-yourself cabinet-makers should be careful not to use new wood, which will contain corrosive moisture.

ALBUMS, PLASTIC CASES AND CARRYING CASES

There are many of these on the market, some both handsome and inexpensive.

There are also attractive Italian and German-made carrying cases for collectors.
These can be obtained from a number of dealers such as Token Publishing. Tel: 01404 46972.
www.tokenpublishing.com

Coin albums, where the coins are contained in cards with crystal-clear film windows, claim to prevent oxidisation. The cards slide into pages in the album, which is a convenient method of storage, especially for new collectors.

Lindner Publications, Unit 3A, Hayle Industrial Park, Hayle, Cornwall TR27 5JR, supplies useful coin and collecting boxes, as well as albums. Tel: 01736 751910. Fax: 01736 751911. www.prinz.co.uk

An extended range of Lighthouse coin accessories, including presentation and carrying cases, is available from the Duncannon Partnership, 4 Beaufort Road, Reigate, Surrey RH2 9DJ. Tel: 01737 244222. www.duncannon.co.uk

Crystalair Compression packs or membrane boxes immobilise items between two layers of clear, inert, polyurethane film that moulds to the object placed between it. They are perfect for storing and transporting valuable and delicate items that also need to be viewed.

For details contact Lane Packaging, Headley Park 8, Headley Road East, Woodley, Reading, Berkshire RG5 4SA. Tel: 0118 944 2425. www.lanepackaging.com

ENVELOPES

Transparent plastic envelopes are very useful for exhibitions, but not recommended for long-term storage purposes.

They tend to make the coins 'sweat' which can lead to corrosion.

Manila envelopes are much more suitable since the paper is dry. Most collectors use them with a cardboard box, a simple, unobtrusive and inexpensive method of storing a collection.

The best article on coin and medal storage is

ABOVE: Another type of attaché case

will usually improve a dirty gold coin. But it is vital that gold coins are not rubbed in any way.

SILVER COINS

Silver coins discolour easily, and are susceptible to damp or chemicals in the atmosphere. Gentle brushing with a soft, non-nylon, bristle brush will clear loose dirt. If the dirt is deep and greasy, a dip in ammonia and careful drying on cotton wool should work. There is no need to clean a coin that has a darkish tone.

COPPER AND BRONZE COINS

There is no safe method of cleaning copper or bronze coins without harming them. Use only a non-nylon, pure bristle brush to deal with dirt.

There is no way of curing verdigris (green spots) or bronze disease (blackish spots) permanently, so do not buy pieces with these problems, unless they are very inexpensive.

Remember that looking after your coins could make you money in the future!

ABOVE: Lindner supply coin albums

by L R Green, who is Higher Conservation Officer at the Department of Coins and Medals at the British Museum. It appeared in the May 1991 issue of *Spink's Numismatic Circular*.

CLEANING COINS

Every week, coin dealers examine coins that someone has unwittingly ruined by cleaning.

Never clean coins unless they are very dirty or corroded. 'Dirt' does not mean oxide, which on silver coins can give a pleasing bluish tone favoured by collectors.

Do not clean extremely corroded coins found in the ground, because if they are important, they will be handed over to a museum conservationist.

GOLD COINS

Gold should cause collectors few problems, since it is subject to corrosion only in extreme conditions such as a long spell in the sea.

A bath in methylated spirits

ABOVE: Coin cases are also available from Lindner

READING MATERIAL

Our directory of suggested books has a range of essential and specialist titles for all aspects of the hobby

We have included the prices you can expect to pay, but some of the books are long out of print and can only be obtained secondhand, indicated by SH

■ Abramson, T, SCBI: 69 – The Abramson Collection: Coins of Early Anglo Saxon England and the North Sea Area. Hardback, jacketed, 294pp, £50.

■ Abramson, T, The Sceatta List, 2012. 280pp. A comprehensive, illustrated, catalogue of early Anglo-Saxon silver coinage. £35

■ Allen, M, The Durham Mint, British Numismatic Society Special Publication No.4, 2003. 222pp, £45

■ Bateson, J D, Coinage in Scotland, 1997. 175pp, well illustrated. The most up-to-date narrative account of Scottish coins in print. £25.

■ Bateson, J D, Scottish Coins, Shire Publications number 189, 1987. 32pp, illustrated. A useful little introduction to the subject. The Shire publications are always good value. £2.95.

■ Besly, E, Coins and Medals of the English Civil War, Second edition – completely revised and updated, 2019, 260pp, illustrated, £40.

■ Besly, E, Loose Change, a Guide to Common Coins and Medals, 1997. 57pp, £6.95.

■ Bland, R, Besly, E and Burnett, A, The Cunetio and Normanby Hoards, with notes to aid identification by Moorhead, S, 304pp, hardback, two of the largest Roman coin hoards from Britain newly available in one volume, £60.

■ Blackburn, M, Viking Coinage and Currency in the British Isles, British Numismatic Special Publication number 7, 2011. 416 pp. £29.

■ Blunt, C E, Stewart, B H I H, Lyon, C S S, Coinage in

10th Century England, 1989. 372pp, 27 plates. £50

■ Buck, I, Medieval English Groats, 2000. 66pp, illustrated. £15.

■ Bull, M, The Half–Crowns of Charles I 1625-1649, Volume 1-5, 2009. Highly detailed and illustrative analysis of the series. £85.

■ Byatt, D, Promises to Pay: The First Three Hundred Years of Bank of England Notes, 1994. 246pp, beautifully illustrated. SH.

■ British Academy, publisher, Sylloge of Coins of the British Isles. 50 volumes, many still in print

■ Brooke, G C, English Coins, reprinted 1966. 300pp, 72 plates. An important one-volume guide to English coinage. SH.

■ Carroll, J and Parsons, D N, Anglo–Saxon Mint Names, volume 1: Axbridge–Hythe, 2007. £25

■ Challis, C, A New History of the Royal Mint, 1992. 806pp, 70 figures and maps. £95.

■ Cheek, J, Monarchy, Money and Medals: Coins Banknotes and Medals from the Collection of Her Majesty The Queen, 2018. 184pp, colour illustrations throughout. £40.

■ Chick, D, The Coinage of Offa, British Numismatic Society Special Publication number 6, 2010. 232 pp, illustrated. £40.

■ C.H.V. and Carson, R.A.G., Roman Imperial Coinage Vol. I: From 31 BC to AD, hardback, jacketed, 360pp, reprinted to 2018, £150.

■ Clancy, K, A History of the Sovereign, Chief Coin of

the World. The Royal Mint, 2015. Full-colour illustrations throughout, 112pp. £25.

■ Clancy, K, *Objects of War: Currency in a Time of Conflict, 2018*, 136pp. Softcover, colour illustrations throughout. £25.

■ Coincraft, publisher, *Standard Catalogue of English and UK Coins*, 1999. 741pp, fully illustrated. £19.50.

■ Coincraft, publisher, *Standard Catalogue of the Coins of Scotland, Ireland, Channel Islands and Isle of Man*, 1999. 439pp, illustrated. £34.50.

■ Colman, F, *Royal Cabinet Stockholm, SCBI 54, Anglo-Saxon Coins, Edward the Confessor and Harold II*. £60

■ Cooper, D, *Coins and Minting*, Shire Publications number 106, 1996. 32pp, illustrated. An excellent account of minting. £2.25.

■ Davies, P, *British Silver Coins Since 1816*, 1982. Still a useful reference for varieties in this area. £22.

■ Dolley, M, *The Norman Conquest and English Coinage*, 1966. 40pp, illustrated. SH.

■ Dowle, A, and Finn, P, *The Guide Book to the Coinage of Ireland*, 1969. First standard catalogue of Irish, still useful, good bibliography. SH.

■ Dyer, G P, editor, *Royal Sovereign 1489–1989*, 1989. 99pp, fully illustrated. £30.

■ Elias, E R D, *The Anglo-Gallic Coins*, 1984. 262pp, fully illustrated. Essential for collectors of this series. £30.

■ Farey, R, A, *A Guide to the Guinea (1663–1813) 2020*. £40. The first major work on the Guinea, a must for the collector. Lavishly illustrated in colour, 148pp. RRP £29.95.

■ Freeman, A, *The Moneyer and Mint in the Reign of Edward the Confessor 1042–1066*. Two parts, 1985. £40. A complete survey of the coinage of the reign.

■ Freeman, M, *The Bronze Coinage of Great Britain*. Reprinted with updated values 2006. 256 pp, illustrated. Extremely useful handbook for the varieties on the bronze coinage. £35.

■ Frey, A R, *Dictionary of Numismatic Names*, reprinted 1973. 405pp. The best numismatic dictionary; search for a secondhand copy. SH.

■ Giodarno, J S, *Portraits of a Prince: Coins, Medals and Banknotes of Edward VIII*, 2009. 704pp, fully illustrated, values in US$. £49.50.

■ Greenhalgh, D, *Medieval Half Groats, Edward III–Richard III*, 2010. 174 pp, illustrated. £45.

■ Grinsell, L V, *The History and Coinage of the Bristol Mint*, 1986. 60pp, illustrated. £5.

■ Grüber, H A, *Handbook of the Coins of Great Britain and Ireland*, revised edition, 1970. 272pp, 64 plates. A superb book. SH.

■ Hobbs, R, *British Iron Age Coins in the British Museum*, 1996. 246pp, 137 plates. Invaluable. Lists over 4,500 pieces. £40.

■ Holmes, R, *Scottish Coins, a History of Small Change in Scotland*, 1998. An invaluable guide to historic small change. 112pp, illustrated. £5.99.

■ Holmes, N M McQ, SCBI 58, *Scottish Coins in the Museums of Scotland*, Part 1, 1526–1603, 2006. 58pp, 99 plates. £55.

■ Kent, J P C and Carson, R A G, *Roman Imperial Coinage Vol. X: The Divided Empire and the Fall of the Western Parts 395–491*, hardback, jacketed, 856pp, reprinted for 2018, £195.

■ de Jersey, P, *Celtic Coinage in Britain*, Shire Publications, 1996. 56pp, illustrated. £4.99.

■ Linecar, H W A, *British Coin Designs and Designers*, 1977. 146pp, fully illustrated. SH

■ Linecar, H W A, *The Crown Pieces of Great Britain and the Commonwealth of Nations*, 1969. 102pp, fully illustrated. The only book dealing solely with all British crowns. SH.

■ Linecar, H W A, editor, *The Milled Coinage of England 1662–1946*, reprinted 1976. 146pp, illustrated. Useful with degrees of rarity. SH.

■ Linecar, H W A, and Stone, A G, *English Proof and Pattern Crown-Size Pieces, 1658–1960*, 1968. 116pp, fully illustrated. SH.

■ Manville, H E, and Robertson, T J, *Encyclopedia of British Numismatics, volume 1: British Numismatic Auction Catalogues from 1710 to the Present*, 1986. 420pp, illustrated. £40.

■ Manville, H E, *Encyclopedia of British Numismatics, volume 2.1: Numismatic Guide to British and Irish Periodicals, 1731–1991*, 1993. 570pp, illustrated. £60.

■ Manville, H E, *Encyclopedia of British Numismatics, volume 2.2: Numismatic Guide to British and Irish Periodicals, 1836–1995*, 1997. 634pp, 31 illustrations. An important reference. £60.

■ Manville, H E, *Encyclopedia of British Numismatics volume 2.3: Numismatic Guide to British and Irish Printed Books, 1600–2004*, 2005. 291pp. £60

■ Manville, H E, *Encyclopaedia of British Numismatics volume 2.4: Biographical Dictionary of British Numismatics*, Spink, 2009. 358pp. £60.

■ Manville, H E, *Tokens of the Industrial Revolution: Foreign Silver Coins Countermarked for Use in Great Britain, c1787–1828*. 308pp, 50 plates. A highly important work. £40.

■ Token Publishing, Marsh, M A, revised by S. Hill, *The Gold Sovereign, 2021*. A must for the sovereign collector, an updated with colour illustrations. 248pp. £16.95.

■ Marsh, M A, *The Gold Half-Sovereign*, 2nd edition, 2004. 119pp, 54 plates. £18.50.

■ Martin, S F, *The Hibernia Coinage of William Wood, 1722–1724*, 2007. 492pp, illustrated. £60.

■ Mass, J P, *The J P Mass Collection: English Short Cross Coins, 1180–1247*, 2001. 2,200 specimens from the author's collection. £50.

■ McCammon, A L T, *Currencies of the Anglo-Norman Isles*, 1984. 2 volumes, 358pp, fully illustrated. Essential for students and collectors.

■ Mucha, M, *Hermitage Museum, St Petersburg, Part IV: English, Irish and Scottish Coins, 1066–1485*, 2005. 23 plates. £40.

■ Naismith, R, *The Coinage of Southern England 796–865*, British Numismatic Society Special Publication number 8, 2011. 2 volumes. 588 pp, 104 plates. £90.

■ North, J J, *English Hammered Coins, volume 1: Early Anglo-Saxon to Henry III, cAD600–1272*, 1994. 320pp, 20 plates. A great reference for collectors. £45.

■ North, J J, *English Hammered Coins, volume 2: Edward I–Charles II, 1272–1662*, 1993. 224pp, 11 plates. A great reference for collectors. £45.

■ North, JJ, *English Hammered Coinage Volume I*, 320pp, hardback, newly reissued for 2018, £50.

■ North, JJ, *English Hammered Coinage Volume II*, 256pp, hardback, newly reissued for 2018, £50.

■ North, J J, and Preston-Morley, P J, *The John G Brooker Collection: Coins of Charles I*, 1984. £25.

■ Naismith, R, *Sylloge of Coins of the British Isles 67 – British Museum, Anglo-Saxon Coins II: Southern English Coinage from Offa to Alfred C. 760–880*, 2016. 272pp. £50.

■ Peck, C W, *English Copper, Tin and Bronze Coins in the British Museum, 1558–1958*, 1960. 648pp, 50 plates. Essential.

Mary Gillick
sculptor and
medallist
Philip Attwood

The British Museum   SPINK

COINS OF
ENGLAND
& THE UNITED KINGDOM
PRE-DECIMAL ISSUES

STANDARD CATALOGUE OF BRITISH COINS
SPINK
2023

MAURICE BULL

ENGLISH
GOLD
COINAGE
FROM 1816
INCORPORATING THE BRITISH
SOVEREIGN SERIES ISSUED
WITHIN THE BRITISH EMPIRE

VOLUME II
SPINK

The seminal work on the subject. SH.

■ Pudill, R, and Eyre, C, *The Tribes and Coins of Celtic Britain*, 2005. 81pp, fully illustrated, price list inc. £15.

■ Rayner, P A, *English Silver Coins since 1649*, 1992. 254pp, 3rd edition. Essential. 3,000 coins listed, 400 illustrated. Covers varieties, rarities, patterns and proofs and mintage figures. £25.

■ Robinson, B, *Silver Pennies and Linen Towels: The Story of the Royal Maundy*, 1992. 274pp, 118 illustrations. A very important work on the subject, entertaining. £29.95.

■ SCBI, Vol. 64. Grosvenor Museum, Chester, Pt. II. Anglo-Saxon Coins and Post-Conquest Coins to 1180, by Hugh Pagan. British Academy. 2012. 156 pp. 34 plates. £50.

■ SCBI, Vol. 65. Norwegian Collections, Pt. I, Anglo-Saxon Coins to 1016, by Elina Screen. British Academy. 2012. 426 pp. 34 plates. £90.

■ SCBI, Vol. 66. Norwegian Collections, Pt. II, Anglo-Saxon and Later Coins, 1015–1279, by Elina Screen. British Academy. 2015. 426 pp. 34 plates. £90.

■ SCBI, Vol. 68. The Lyon Collection of Anglo-Saxon Coins, by Stewart Lyon, British Academy. 2017. 326 pp. 42 plates. £90.

■ Spink, publisher, *Standard Catalogue of British Coins*, 2006. 42nd edition. Fully illustrated. Still the first point of reference for collectors.

■ Spink, publisher, SCBI 61, *The Herbert Schneider Collection, volume 3: Anglo-Gallic, Flemish and*

Brabantine Gold Coins 1330–1794. Cataloguing and illustrating 348 coins with transcriptions of legends and details of classification and die-linking. £60.

■ Spink, publisher, *English Gold Coinage 1649–1816* (Volume I), 2020. 680pp, with colour illustrations throughout. Brand new comprehensive guide covering every type of English gold coin up to 1816. £50.

■ Spink, publisher, *English Gold Coinage Volume II, from 1816, incorporating the British Sovereign series issued within the British Empire*, 616 pages with colour illustrations throughout. Comprehensive guide covers every type of English gold coin 1816 onwards, including the British Sovereign series issued within the British Empire, along with current prices. RRP £50.

■ Spink, publisher, in association with the British Museum. *Mary Gillick: Sculptor and Medallist* Author: Philip Attwood. 216 pages with colour illustrations throughout. The first published study of this neglected British artist, best known for the portrait of Queen Elizabeth II that appeared on UK coins from the beginning of her reign until decimalisation in 1971. RRP £25.

■ Spink, publisher, *The Standard Catalogue Coins of England*, 648 pages with colour illustrations throughout. The historic reference work for British coins, featuring every major coin type from Celtic to Queen Elizabeth II, with prices updated annually. RRP £35.

■ Spink, publisher, *Coins of Scotland, Ireland and the*

Islands (4th Edition), 2020. 312pp, colour illustrations throughout. An essential guide for collectors in this area with new information and current prices. £40.

■ Spink, publisher, *English Silver Coinage Since 1649*, 2020. 620pp, with black and white illustrations throughout. Complete update with new varieties, corrections and rarity values. £50.

■ Spink, publisher, British Numismatic Society, *The BNS, Interpreting Medieval Coinage, Studies in Memory of Stewart Lyon*, edited by M. Allen, R. Naismith and H. Pagan.

■ Stewart, I H, *The Scottish Coinage*, 1967. 2nd edition. 215pp, 22 plates. Long out of print, but still essential for the serious collector. SH.

■ Stewartby, Lord, *English Coins 1180–1551*, 2009. 624 pp, illustrated. An indispensable overview of English medieval coins. £45.

■ Sutherland, C H V, *English Coinage, 600–1900*, 1973. 232pp, 108 plates. Beautifully written and the best narrative account of coinage. SH.

■ Thompson, J D A, *Inventory of British Coin Hoards*, AD 600–1500, 1956. 165pp, 24 plates. SH.

■ Van Arsdell, R D, *Celtic Coinage of Britain*, 1989. 584pp, 54 plates. A pioneering, controversial work; important for the images alone. SH.

■ Williams, J, *Money, A History*, 1997. 256pp, fully illustrated. Accompanies the British Museum's HSBC Money Gallery. £25.

■ Wilson, A and Rasmussen, M, *English Pattern Trial and Proof Coins in Gold*, 1547–1968, 2000. 537pp, illustrated. Covers a fascinating series. £85.

■ Withers, P and B, *British Coin Weights*, 1993. A corpus of the coin-weights made for use in England, Scotland and Ireland. 366pp, illustrated. For the serious student. £95.

■ Withers, P and B, *Farthings and Halfpennies, Edward I & II*, 2005. 60pp, illustrated. Helpful series guide. £12.

■ Withers, P and B, *Farthings and Halfpennies, Edward III & Richard II*, 2002. 56 pp, illustrated. £12.

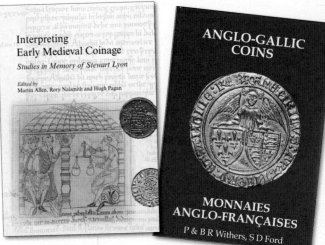

■ Withers, P and B, *Halfpennies and Farthings, Henry IV, V & VI*, 2003. 68pp, illustrated. £12.

■ Withers, P and B, *Halfpennies and Farthings, Edward IV–Henry VII*, 2004. 56pp, illustrated. £12.

■ Withers, P and B, *Small Silver, Henry VIII–the Commonwealth*, 2004. 56pp, illustrated. £12.

■ Withers, P and B, *Irish Small Silver, John–Edward VI*, 2004. 56pp, illustrated. £12.

■ Withers, P and B, *The Galata Guide to the Pennies of Edward I & Edward II and the Coins of the Mint of Berwick-upon-Tweed*, 2006. 64pp, fully illustrated. £20.

■ Withers, P and B, and Ford, S, *Anglo-Gallic Coins/ Monnaies Anglo-Francaises*, 2015. Well-illustrated in English and occasional French. 200pp. £55.

■ Woodhead, P, *The Herbert Schneider Collection of English Gold Coins, Part 1: Henry III–Elizabeth I*, 1996. 466pp, 83 plates. A great catalogue of the best collection in private hands. £60.

■ Woodhead, P, *The Herbert Schneider Collection of English Gold Coins, Part 2: 1603–20th Century*, 2002. 58 plates. Essential. Describes and illustrates 674 coins. £60

■ Wren, CR, *The Voided Long-Cross Coinage 1247–1279*, 88pp, paperback, newly reissued for 2018, £20.

■ Wren, CR, *The Short-Cross Coinage 1180–1247*, 96pp, paperback, newly reissued for 2018, £20.

■ Wren, CR, *The English Long-Cross Pennies 1279–1489*, 200pp, paperback, newly reissued for 2018, £25.

MUSEUM COLLECTIONS

Here is a round-up of the best places to see coins on display in the British Isles

ABOVE: The Ryther Hoard, found in 1992 consists of 812 silver coins from Edward I to Henry VI, is on display at the York Museum.

LONDON, THE BRITISH MUSEUM

The Department of Coins and Medals at the British Museum boasts the country's premier numismatic collection numbering around 800,000 objects, a selection of which is on permanent display including the unique Anglo-Saxon gold penny of King Offa. The Money Gallery in Room 68 chronicles the development and use of money throughout the world.

The collection also contains significant hoards such as the late-Roman Cunetio hoard which, at 55,000 coins, remains the largest hoard ever found in the UK, the Alton hoard of Celtic gold staters and the Appledore hoard of 11th century pennies. The Vale of York hoard, jointly owned with The Yorkshire Museum, provides a valuable insight into the Viking world.

Collectors can access and photograph (for non-commercial use) the reserve collections in the departmental study room, Tuesday to Thursday by appointment.

Tom Hockenhull, Keeper of Coins and Medals, oversees the Coins and Medals Department. Dept. Coins and Medals, British Museum, Great Russell Street London WC1B 3DG.
■ Tel: Tel: 0207 323 8607

■ www.britishmuseum.org
■ Email: coins@thebritishmuseum.org

EDINBURGH, NATIONAL MUSEUM OF SCOTLAND
The Museum of Scotland has the most important collection of Scottish coins in the country. Highlights include one of the two known specimens of the Henry and Mary ryal of 1565, acquired in 2002. A selection of coins is on display alongside other exhibits.

For all enquiries, contact the National Museum of Scotland, Chambers Street, Edinburgh EH1 1JF.
■ www.nms.ac.uk

GLASGOW, HUNTERIAN MUSEUM
The Hunterian houses one of the world's most important numismatic collections, containing c.100,000 coins, medals, tokens and related objects. At its core are 30,000 items from William Hunter's original Enlightenment bequest assembled between 1770 and 1783.

The Hunterian's holdings include extensive ranges of Ancient Greek, Roman, Byzantine, Anglo–Saxon, medieval Scottish and English, and modern coins, as well as medals from the Renaissance to contemporary Scotland. Many of these are unique or extremely rare and most are in superb condition.

A limited selection of numismatic material is on display. Researchers may access the collection by appointment.

The Curator of Numismatics is Jesper Ericsson, The Hunterian, University of Glasgow, Glasgow, G12 8QQ.
■ Tel: 0141 330 2303
■ www.gla.ac.uk/hunterian
■ Email: Email: Jesper.Ericsson@glasgow.ac.uk

AMGUEDDFA CYMRU – MUSEUM WALES
The numismatic collection comprises coins, tokens, medals and related objects. It ranges widely, from ancient times to the present, with five main areas of strength: Celtic coins; Greek and Roman coins; coins of England and the British Isles; tokens, banknotes and 'paranumismatica', primarily Welsh; and commemorative medals and awards, especially relating to Wales and the exploits of Welsh people. There are also small comparative collections of European, British Colonial and world coins.

The collection includes numerous hoards, archaeological site finds and single coin finds from the Roman period onwards. Coins found in or relating to Wales remain an important element of current collecting. Occasional Welsh finds of treasure, such as the English Civil War hoard from Tregwynt, Pembrokeshire (buried around 1648 and rediscovered in 1996), provide spectacular individual acquisitions.

Amgueddfa Cymru's research collection is held at the National Museum Cardiff. Visitors are welcome by appointment.

Public displays of coins from the numismatics collection can be viewed at St Fagans National Museum of History, the National Roman Legion Museum (Caerleon) and the National Waterfront Museum (Swansea).

The Senior Curator of Numismatics and the Welsh Economy is Alastair Willis. Department of History and Archaeology, National Museum Cardiff, Cathays Park, Cardiff CF10 3NP.
■ Tel: 029 2057 3291.
■ www.museumwales.ac.uk

BIRMINGHAM, MUSEUM AND ART GALLERY
Birmingham Museum has one of the largest regional collections in England, with important Celtic, Saxon, Norman and Medieval coins. Some items can be viewed online but visits are by appointment only.

The Staffordshire Hoard, the largest hoard of Anglo–Saxon gold artefacts ever found, discovered in July 2009, has been safely secured and there is a permanent display of items from the find.

The Curator of Antiquities and Numismatics is Dr Rebecca Bridgman, Birmingham Museum and Art Gallery, Chamberlain Square, Birmingham B3 3DH.
■ Tel: 0121 348 8000.
■ www.bmag.org.uk

CAMBRIDGE, THE FITZWILLIAM MUSEUM
The Department of Coins and Medals has an internationally important numismatic collection, many of which are on permanent display. Coins on display include an outstanding selection of ancient and Medieval coins, such as a gold penny of Henry III and the 14th century hoard found at Chesterton Lane Corner in Cambridge.

A major strength is the museum's Anglo–Saxon and Norman coins, with many pieces from the Christopher

Blunt and William Conte collections. Acquisitions in recent years include the Lester Watson collection of military medals, with two Victoria Crosses and other rarities. These medals and other items from the collection can be viewed on the Department's website. Visitors are welcome by appointment. The Keeper of Coins and Medals is Dr Adrian Popescu, Fitzwilliam Museum, Trumpington Street, Cambridge CB2 1RB.

- Tel: 01223 332900.
- www.fitzmuseum.cam.ac.uk/dept/coins

OXFORD, THE ASHMOLEAN MUSEUM

The museum's Heberden Coin Room contains a wide range of Roman, Celtic and Medieval coins.

Highlights include a magnificent 1645 'Oxford crown' of Charles I and a selection of Anglo-Saxon gold thrymsas from the Crondall Hoard of 1828.

Since the museum re-opened in late 2009, the Coin Room now has a major new Money Gallery where many of the coins and related numismatic items are on show in a superb thematic exhibition.

A recent acquisition is the spectacular Asthall Tudor hoard of 210 gold angels and half-angels.

The Keeper of the Heberden Coin Room is Professor Chris Howgego, Ashmolean Museum, Beaumont Street, Oxford OX1 2PH.

- Tel: 01865 278058.
- www.ashmolean.org/departments/ heberdencoinroom/coinroom@ashmus.ox.ac.uk

YORK, YORKSHIRE MUSEUM

The Vale of York Viking Hoard is jointly owned with British Museum. It is the most significant Viking treasure to be found in Britain in over 150 years. Since its 2007 discovery it has been shown in Berlin, Copenhagen and is now on display at the British Museum as part of the exhibition "Vikings: Life and Legend".

The Yorkshire museum is strong on Roman coinage, Northumbrian stycas, English hammered silver coins and trade tokens. Hoards such as the 4th century Heslington hoard and single finds from Yorkshire are well represented, as well as Roman, Viking and medieval artefacts. The Ryther Hoard is on display, it consists of 812 silver groats, half-groats and pennies from Edward I to Henry VII contained in a Humber ware jug, It was found by a metal detectorist in North Yorkshire in 1992.

The Curator of Numismatics is Dr Andy Woods,

Yorkshire Museum, Museum Gardens, York YO1 7FR.
- Tel: 01904 687627.
- www.yorkshiremuseum.org.uk

BELFAST, ULSTER MUSEUM

The museum houses the best collection of banknotes in Ireland. A representative array of coins is now incorporated into a narrative exhibition of Irish history since 1550 to recent times. The main collection is accessible by arrangement.

For all enquiries contact the Ulster Museum, Botanic Gardens, Belfast BT9 5AB.
- Tel: 028 9044 0000.
- www.nmi.com/um/Collections/History/ Coins-and-Medals

DUBLIN, NATIONAL MUSEUM OF IRELAND

The museum has a permanent exhibition telling the story of coins and money in Ireland from the 10th Century. Highlights are seven of the eleven known specimens of the exceedingly rare Ormonde gold pistoles.

There is currently no Curator of Coins. Enquiries should be addressed to the Duty Officer, Art and Industrial Division, National Museum of Ireland, Collins Barracks, Benburb Street, Dublin 7, Ireland.
- Tel: +353 1677 7444.
- www.museum.ie

OTHER IMPORTANT UK MUSEUMS

Other museums with good collections include:
- Blackburn Museum & Art Gallery, Museum Street, Blackburn, Lancashire BB1 7AJ.
Tel: 01254 667130. museum@blackburn.gov.uk
- City Museum, Queen's Road, Bristol BS8 1RL.
Tel: 01179 223571.
- The Leeds Museum Discovery Centre, Carlisle Road, Leeds, West Yorkshire LS10 1LB.
Tel: 0113 378 2100.
- Manchester Museum, The University of Manchester, Oxford Road, Manchester M13 9PL.
Tel: 0161 275 2634.
- Manx Museum, Douglas, Isle of Man IM1 3LY.
Tel: 01624 648000.
- Reading Museum, Town Hall, Blagrave Street, Reading, Berkshire RG1 1QH. Tel: 0118 937 3400.
- Royal Albert Memorial Museum, Queen Street, Exeter, Devon EX4 3RX. Tel: 01392 265858.

COUNTERFEIT COINS

Forgeries have always been a problem. Here is some advice on the most commonly counterfeited coins

ABOVE: 'Fantasy' Celtic stater

There have been forgeries since the earliest days of coin production, so, of course, new forgeries appear on the scene every year. There is always someone willing to try to deceive the collector and the dealer.

However, nowadays few forgers end up making much money.

As a result of the diligence and ongoing monitoring of the situation by the British Numismatic Trade Association and the International Association of Professional Numismatists, the trade is now more informed about the latest forgeries before they have had a chance to be a serious menace.

It has recently come to light that there are forgeries of British coins on the market, allegedly emanating from China.

ABOVE: Dennington Edward III noble

They include forgeries of modern British silver and copper coins in lower grades, including common coins. Two or more identical coins show the same defects, or purported 'damage', revealing them as fakes. It seems that the counterfeiters sell on the internet, picking up clients in various countries who are then set up as distributors. At the moment there is not a full list available.

ABOVE: Ceolwulf penny forgery

Examples reported are: George III half crowns, 1763 'Northumberland' Shilling, the rare 1816 Bank Token three shillings, George V 'wreath' crowns and Victoria 'old head' half crowns. There is also a convincing 1826 penny, with a die-axis deviation to 7mm off-centre and a weight of 18.04g instead of 18.8g; a 1854 penny with a die-axis deviation to 3mm off-centre, weighing 19.02g instead of 18.8.g and an Isle of Man 1813 penny with a die-axis deviation to 3mm off-centre, weight 19.11g instead of 20.3g–20.6g.

They can easily deceive as they appear to have signs of circulation and are toned, and are therefore not easily detectable.

Two hammered gold coins, apparently from the same source, have also been deemed forgeries. They are an Edward VI third period half-sovereign and an Elizabeth I angel.

As always, collectors should buy with caution and from reputable dealers.

ABOVE: A new forgery of the 1826 penny

Forgeries were last a matter of major concern in the late 1960s and early 1970s. A considerable number of forged 1887 £5 and £2 pieces, early sovereigns and some silver pieces, in particular the 'Gothic' crown, thought to be manufactured in Beirut, came on to the market.

Also in the early 1970s, the Dennington forgeries

could have made a serious impact on the English hammered gold market, but luckily they were detected early on. Fortunately, only a few of these are still in circulation.

In the late 1970s a crop of forgeries of ancient British coins came to light, causing a panic in academic and trade circles.

This caused a lack of confidence in the trade and it took a number of years for the confidence to return.

A spate of copies of Anglo-Saxon coins from the West Country were being sold as replicas in the early 1990s, but they are still deceptive in the wrong hands.

ABOVE: A copy of an Apollo Ambiani stater

Bob Forrest compiled a list of them and it was published in the IAPN *Bulletin of Forgeries* in 1995–96, volume 20, number 2.

THE DIFFERENT TYPES OF FORGERY

Forgeries can be divided into two main groups: contemporary forgeries which are intended to be used as face-value money and forgeries which are intended to deceive collectors.

The following five methods of reproduction have been used for coins which attempt to deceive collectors:

■ Electrotyping. These could deceive an expert.
■ Casting. Old casts are easily recognisable, as they have marks made by air bubbles on the surface, and showing a generally 'fuzzy' effect. Modern cast copies are much more of a problem. They are produced by sophisticated pressure-casting, which can be extremely difficult to distinguish from the originals.
■ The fabrication of false dies. With hammered coins, counterfeits are not difficult for an expert to detect. However, the sophisticated die-production techniques used in Beirut have resulted in good forgeries of modern gold and silver coins.
■ The use of genuine dies put to illegal use, such as re-striking.

■ Alteration of a genuine coin, most commonly a George V penny. The 1933 is extremely rare, so other years are often altered to provide the rarer date.

COUNTERFEIT COIN CLUB

There is a Counterfeit Coin Club that produces a small quarterly journal. For membership details write to its President: Ken Peters, 8 Kings Road, Biggin Hill, Kent TN16 3XU.
E-mail: kenvoy@hotmail.co.uk

DENNINGTON FORGERIES

A man called Anthony Dennington was tried at the Central Criminal Court in the 1970s and found guilty of six charges of 'causing persons to pay money by falsely pretending that they were buying genuine antique coins'.

A small number of these pieces are still in the trade, and since they have deceived some collectors and dealers, we have recorded them here, as they appeared in the *International Bureau for the Suppression of Counterfeit Coins Bulletin* in August 1976.

These copies are generally very good and you must beware of them. The following points may be useful guidelines:
■ The coins are usually slightly 'shiny' in appearance, and the edges are not good, because they have been filed down and polished.
■ They are usually very 'hard' to touch, whereas there is a certain amount of 'spring' in the genuine articles.
■ They usually, but not always, feel slightly thick. They do not quite feel like an electrotype but are certainly thicker than normal.
■ Although the Mary fine sovereign reproduction is heavier, at 16.1986g, these pieces are usually lighter in weight than the originals.

MODERN COINS

As far as forgeries of modern coins are concerned, the most worrying aspect has been

ABOVE: A Dennington Mary fine sovereign of 1553

the enormous increase in well–produced forgeries in the last 25 years.

They are so well produced that it is often impossible for the naked eye to detect the difference, and it has therefore become the job of the scientist and metallurgist.

Many of these pieces have deceived dealers and collectors, but they do not seem to have caused a crisis of confidence.

ABOVE: A forged 1832 sovereign

ABOVE: A copy of an Una and Lion 1839 five pounds

This increase in the number of modern counterfeits has been due to the massive rise in coin values since the 1960s.

The vast majority of these forgeries emanate from the Middle East, where it is not illegal to produce counterfeits of other countries' coins. But the coin trade is alert and reports are circulated quickly whenever a new forgery is spotted.

But with the profits available to the forger, no one should be complacent. At the time of writing, it only

takes about £950 worth of gold to make an 1887–dated five pound piece of correct composition, valued at approximately £1,650.

Detecting forgeries requires specialist knowledge, so we can only point out to you which coins are commonly counterfeited. In the catalogue section of *British Coins Market Values*, we have placed F beside a number of coins which have been counterfeited and which frequently turn up.

Watch out for sovereigns, in particular, of which there are forgeries of every date from 1900 to 1932 and even recent dates such as 1957 and 1976.

Pieces you should be particularly careful about, especially if they are being offered below the normal catalogue value, are listed in the boxes.

Most modern forgeries of, for example, Gothic crowns, are offered at prices that are 10% or 20% below the current market price.

The moral is: if something looks too good to be true, it probably is!

DENNINGTON FORGERIES STILL IN THE TRADE

- Henry III gold penny
- Edward III Treaty period noble
- Edward III Treaty period noble with saltire before King's name
- Henry IV heavy coinage noble
- Henry V noble, Class C, mullet at King's sword arm
- Henry VI mule noble
- Henry VI noble, annulet issue, London
- Edward IV royal, Norwich
- Edward IV royal, York
- Elizabeth I angel
- Mary fine sovereign 1553
- James I unite, mintmark mullet
- James I rose royal, third coinage, mint mark lis
- James I third coinage laurel
- Commonwealth unite 1651
- Commonwealth half–unite 1651
- Charles II touch piece

ABOVE: A forged 1820 £5

ABOVE: A copy of a 1847 Gothic Crown, edge UNDECIMO

ABOVE: A forged 1913 sovereign

OTHER SAFEGUARDS

The best protection against purchasing forgeries is to buy from a reputable dealer or auctioneer who is a member of the BNTA or the IAPN, or one who will unconditionally guarantee all his coins are genuine.

Legal tender coins, which include £5 and £2 pieces, sovereigns, half sovereigns and crowns, are protected by the Forgery and Counterfeiting Act. Contact the

ABOVE: A counterfeit 1822 sovereign

COMMONLY FORGED COINS

- 1738, 1739 two guineas
- 1793, 1798 guineas, there could also be other dates
- 1820 pattern five pounds
- 1820 pattern two pounds
- 1839 five pounds, plain edge variety
- 1887 five pounds
- 1887 two pounds, many forgeries in circulation
- 1893 five pounds, two pounds
- 1902 five pounds, two pounds
- 1911 five pounds, two pounds
- 1817, 1819 (altered date), 1822, 1825, 1827, 1832, 1887, 1889, 1892, 1892M, 1908C, 1913C sovereigns; 1900–1932 inclusive, plus 1957, 1959, 1963, 1966, 1967, 1974, 1976
- 1847 Gothic crowns
- 1905 half crowns

police if you believe this Act may have been contravened.

If your dealer is unhelpful over a non-legal tender item which you have purchased, and which you think has been falsely described, you can take legal action under the Trades Description Act 1968. This is a long and difficult process. Contact your local Trading Standards Office or Consumer Protection department.

If in doubt always seek advice from a member of the BNTA or the IAPN.

ABOVE: A forged 1827 sovereign

LITERATURE ON FORGERY

The back issues of *Spink's Numismatic Circular* and *Seaby's Coin & Medal Bulletin* are useful sources of information on the forgeries that have been recorded over the years.

The ISBCC also produced a series of forgery bulletins, mainly on modern coins, which can now only be found secondhand.

The most useful work on hammered coins is by L A Lawrence in the *British Numismatic Journal* back in 1905!

ABOVE: A copy of a Mary ryal

RECENT FORGERIES

- George III half crowns
- George III 1763 'Northumberland' shilling
- George III 1816 Bank Token three shillings
- George V 'wreath' crowns
- Victoria 'old head' half crowns
- Edward VI third period half-sovereign
- Elizabeth I angel

COIN GRADING

The basics of grading and details of the different conditions

It is important that newcomers to collecting should get to know the different grades of condition before buying or selling coins.

The system of grading most commonly used in Britain recognises the following main classes in descending order of quality: Brilliant Uncirculated (B Unc, BU), Uncirculated (Unc), Extremely Fine (EF), Very Fine (VF), Fine (F), Fair, Poor.

Beginners often get confused when they first encounter these grades.

The word 'fine' implies a coin of high quality, yet this grade is near the bottom of the scale. Fine is, in fact, about the lowest grade acceptable to most collectors of modern coinage in Britain.

But, to some extent, the grade 'is in the eye of the beholder', and there are always likely to be differences of opinion as to the exact grade of a coin.

Some collectors and dealers have tried to make the existing scale of definitions more exact by adding letters such as N (Nearly), G (Good, meaning slightly better than the grade), A (About or Almost) and so on. In cases where a coin wears more on one side than the other, two grades are shown, the first for the obverse, the second for the reverse such as: GVF/EF.

Any major faults not apparent from the use of a particular grade are often described separately. These include dents and noticeable scratches, discoloration, areas of corrosion, edge knocksand holes.

SPECIAL TERMS

Full mint lustre

There are two schools of thought on the use of the terms Brilliant Uncirculated and Uncirculated. The former is often considered to be the most useful and descriptive term for coins of copper, bronze, nickel–brass or other base metals, which display what is known as 'full mint lustre'.

When this term is being used it is often necessary to employ the grade Uncirculated to describe coins which have never been circulated but have lost the original lustre of a newly minted coin.

However, some dealers and collectors tend to classify as Uncirculated all coins which have not circulated, whether they are brilliant or toned, and do not use the term Brilliant Uncirculated.

Fleur de coin

Sometimes FDC (fleur de coin) is used to define top-grade coins, but it really only applies to pieces in perfect mint state with no flaws or surface scratches.

With modern methods of minting, slight damage to the surface is inevitable, except in the case of proofs, and therefore Brilliant Uncirculated or Uncirculated best describe the highest grade of modern coins.

The word 'proof' should not be used to denote a coin's condition. Proofs are pieces struck on specially prepared blanks from highly polished dies and usually have a mirror–like finish.

Fair and Poor

Fair is applied to very worn coins which still have the main parts of the design distinguished and Poor denotes a grade in which the design and rim are worn almost flat and few details are discernible.

AMERICAN GRADING

The American grading system is quite different to the British one. It purports to be a lot more accurate, but is actually much more prone, in our opinion, to be abused, and we prefer the British dealers' more conservative methods of grading.

American dealers use many more terms, ranging from Mint State to About Good. The latter could be described as 'very heavily worn, with portions of lettering, date and legend worn smooth. The date may be partially legible'. In Britain we would simply say 'Poor'.

There is also a numerical method of describing coins, often used in the United States. For example, an MS–65 coin would be Mint State and a 65 would mean 'an above average Uncirculated coin which may be brilliant or lightly toned but has some surface marks'.

The MS system seemed to be acceptable at first but there are two schools of thought in the United States and you will quite frequently see coins graded in the more traditional manner in sale catalogues.

GRADING EXAMPLES

It would be impossible to show every coin in different grades. We show instead representative examples from three different periods in the British series, to illustrate the middle range of coin conditions.

Each coin is shown in Extremely Fine, Very Fine and Fine condition.

Extremely Fine
This describes coins which have been put into circulation, but have received only the minimum amount of damage since. There may be a few slight marks or minute scratches in the field, – the flat area around the main design – but otherwise the coin should show little sign of having been in circulation.

Very Fine
Coins in very fine condition show some wear on the raised surfaces, but all other detail is very clear. Here, all three coins have had a little wear which can be seen in the details of the hair and face. But they are still in attractive condition from the collector's viewpoint.

Fine
In this grade coins show noticeable wear on the raised parts of the design; most other details should still be clear.

GRADES OF COIN

EXTREMELY FINE (EF)

VERY FINE (VF)

FINE (F)

ABBREVIATIONS & TERMS

These are the abbreviations and terms used in the price guide section

* Asterisks against some dates indicate that no firm prices were available at the time of going to press.

2mm The P of PENNY is 2mm from the trident on some 1895 pennies. Otherwise, the gap is 1mm

AE numismatic symbol for copper or copper alloys

Arabic 1 or Roman I varieties of the 1 in 1887

arcs decorative border of arcs which vary in number

B on William III coins, minted at Bristol

BB beaded border

BBITANNIAR lettering error

Bank of England issued overstruck Spanish dollars for currency use in Britain 1804–1811

black farthings 1897–1918, artificially darkened to avoid confusion with half sovereigns

brilit lettering error

B Unc, BU Brilliant Uncirculated condition

BV bullion value

C on milled gold coins, minted at Ottawa, Canada

C on William III coins, minted at Chester

close colon colon close to DEF

crosslet 4 having upper and lower serifs on the horizontal bar of the 4 (compare plain 4)

cu–ni cupro-nickel

debased in 1920 the silver fineness in British coins was debased from .925 to .500

'Dorrien and Magens' issue of shillings by a group of bankers, which was suppressed on the day of issue

ABOVE: E.I.C. initials

DRITANNIAR lettering error

E minted at Exeter on William III coins

E, E* on Queen Anne coins, minted at Edinburgh

Edin Edinburgh

EEC European Economic Community

EF over price column Extremely Fine condition

ABOVE: English shilling, 1937–46

E.I.C. East India Co, supplier of metal

Eleph, eleph & castle elephant or elephant and castle provenance mark, below the bust. Taken from the badge of the African ('Guinea') Company, which imported the metal for the coins

Eng English shilling. In 1937, English and Scottish versions of the shilling were introduced. English designs have a lion standing on a crown between 1937–1951 and three leopards on a shield between 1953–66

exergue segment below main design, usually containing the date

Ext extremely

F face value only

F over price column Fine condition

F forgeries exist of these pieces. In some cases the forgeries are complete fakes. In others where a particular date is rare, the date of a common coin has been altered. Be very cautious when buying any of these coins

Fair rather worn condition

fantasies non-currency items, often just produced for the benefit of collectors

far colon colon further from DEF than in close colon variety

FDC fleur de coin. A term used to describe coins in perfect mint condition, with no flaws, scratches or other marks

fillet hair band

flan blank for a coin or medal

GEOE lettering error

Gothic Victorian coins featuring Gothic-style portrait and lettering

guinea–head die used for obverse of guinea

ABOVE: Victoria Gothic florin

ABOVE: The Jubilee Head was introduced in 1887 to mark Victoria's Golden Jubilee

ABOVE: KN mintmark

H mintmark of The Mint, Birmingham

hd head

hp, harp for example early, ordinary varieties of the Irish harp on reverse

hearts motif in top right-hand corner of Hanoverian shield on reverse

im initial mark

inc incised, sunk in

inv inverted

JH Jubilee Head

KN mintmark of the Kings Norton Metal Company

L.C.W. Initials of Leonard Charles Wyon, engraver

LIMA coins bearing this word were struck from bullion captured from vessels carrying South American treasure, which may have come from Lima, Peru

low horizon on normal coins the horizon meets the point where Britannia's left leg crosses behind the right. On this variety the horizon is lower

LVIII etc regnal year in Roman numerals on the edge

matt type of proof without a mirror-like finish

M on gold coins minted at Melbourne, Australia

'military' popular name for the 1813 guinea struck for the payment of troops fighting in the Napoleonic Wars

mm mintmark

mod eff modified effigy of George V

mule coin struck from wrongly paired dies

N on William III coins, minted at Norwich

obv obverse, usually the 'head' side of a coin

OH Old Head

OT ornamental trident

P on gold coins, minted at Perth, Australia

pattern trial piece not issued for currency

piedfort a coin which has been specially struck on a thicker than normal blank. In France, where the term originates, the kings seem to have issued them as presentation pieces from the 12th century onwards. In Britain, Medieval and Tudor examples are known, and their issue has been reintroduced by the Royal Mint, starting with the twenty pence piedfort of 1982

plain on silver coins, no provenance marks in angles between shields on reverse

plain 4 with upper serif only to horizontal bar of 4

plumes symbol denoting Welsh mines as the source of the metal

ABOVE: 'Military' guinea, reverse

ABOVE: Plumes provenance mark

proof coin specially struck from highly polished dies. Usually has a mirror-like surface

prov a provenance mark on a coin, such as a rose, plume or elephant, which indicates the supplier of the bullion from which the coin was struck

PT plain trident

raised in relief, not incuse

RB round beads in border

rev reverse, 'tail' side of coin

r & p roses and plumes

rose symbol denoting west of England mines as the source of the metal

PRITANNIAR lettering error

QVARTO fourth regnal year, on edge

QVINTO fifth regnal year, on edge

rsd raised

S on gold coins minted at Sydney, Australia

SA on gold coins mined at Pretoria, South Africa

Scot Scottish shilling. In 1937, English and Scottish versions of the shilling were introduced. Scottish designs have a lion seated on crown, holding a sword and sceptre between 1937–51 and a lion rampant on a shield between 1953–66

SS C South Sea Company, the source of the metal

SECUNDO second regnal year, on edge

SEPTIMO seventh regnal year, on edge

Slabbed a term referring to a coin that has been graded and encapsulated.

'spade' the spade-like shape of the shield on George III gold coins

TB toothed beads in border

TERTIO third regnal year, on edge

trnctn base of head or bust where the neck or shoulders terminate

Unc Uncirculated condition

var variety

VF above price column Very Fine condition

ABOVE: 1723 halfcrown with W.C.C. initials

VIGO struck from bullion captured in Vigo Bay, Spain

VIP 'very important person'. The so-called VIP crowns were the true proofs for the years of issue. Probably most of the limited number struck would have been presented to high-ranking officials

W.C.C. Welsh Copper Company, indicating the supplier of the metal

wire type figure of value in thin wire-like script

W.W., ww initials of William Wyon, engraver

xxri lettering error

y, Y on William III coins minted in York

YH Young Head

MARKET PRICES

CELTIC COINAGE

This remarkable series produced a great variety of issues from different tribes and "kings" in differing areas of Pritania (Britain). Often beautiful, their design and manufacture were primitive, but remarkably consistent in metal content and die production.

The early British series is the hardest to price, as the market has developed considerably since the publication of R D Van Arsdell's *Celtic Coinage of Britain* in 1989, an essential book for collectors, however it has now been superseded by *Ancient British Coins* (ABC) published by Chris Rudd. Others of even greater depth have been published, i.e. *Divided Kingdoms: The Gold Coinage of Southern Britain*, by John Sills and Made for Trade by John Talbot.

The early British series is the hardest to price, as the market has developed considerably since the publication of R D Van Arsdell's *Celtic Coinage of Britain* in 1989, an essential book for collectors.

A number of forgeries of this series exist, some of relatively recent production, and numerous items from undeclared hoards are also on the market. It is therefore essential to buy from a reputable dealer.

We are very grateful for the help of Robert Van Arsdell who produced the synopsis of the material we have used.

We have kept this very basic, and linked it for easy reference with *The Coinage of Ancient Britain* by R P Mack, third edition (now out of print), and with the *British Museum Catalogue of British Iron Age Coins* by R Hobbs, where possible.

In the listings, Mack types are indicated by 'M' and BMC types by 'B', Ancient British Coins is indicated by 'ABC'. The V numbers relate to the Van Arsdell catalogue. The existence of forgeries is indicated by F.

The map on the right shows the distribution of the tribes in Britain based on the map in *The Coinage of Ancient Britain*, by R P Mack, published by Spink and B A Seaby Ltd.

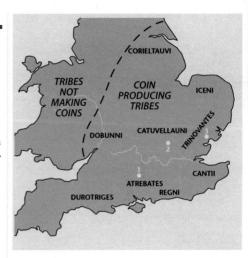

KEY TO TOWNS:
1. Calleva Atrebatum (Silchester)
2. Verulamium (St Albans)
3. Camulodunum (Colchester)

Prices quoted are for centrally struck examples, with no weakness in the design and clear legends (where relevant). When assessing, eye appeal is important, more so than in any other series.

ABOVE: Chute Gold Stater

	F	VF
Abstract type M26, 30, V44, 46, ABC 13	£325	£950
Gallic War type M27, a, V50, 52 F	£300	£700
SUESSIONES		
Abstract type M34a, V85, ABC 25	£575	£900
VE MONOGRAM		
M82, a, b, V8, ABC 19, 7 F	£500	£145
WESTERHAM	F	VF
M28, 29, V200, 202, B1–24	£275	£685

GOLD STATERS WITHOUT LEGENDS IMPORTED FROM THE CONTINENT

ABOVE: Gallo–Belgic Stater

AMBIANI	F	VF
Large flan type M1, 3, V10, 12, ABC 4	£3000	£7000
Defaced die type M5, 7, V30, 33, ABC 10	£900	£3000

BRITISH COINS MARKET VALUES 2023   **49**

Minted in Britain

	F	VF
WESTERHAM		
M28, 29, V200, 202, B1–24	£650	£1300
CHUTE (Belgae)		
M32, V1205, B35–76, ABC 746 F	£400	£800
CLACTON		
Type I M47, V1458, B137–144, ABC 2326 F	£890	£2100
Type II M46, a, V30, 1455, B145–179	£600	£1900
CORIELTAUVI (N E COAST TYPE)		
Type I M50–M51a, V800, B182–191, ABC 1719	£650	£2100
Type II M52–57, S27, V804	£600	£2000

ABOVE: Corieltauvi (South Ferriby) Stater

	F	VF
TRINOVANTES		
WHADDON CHASE		
M133–138, V1470–1478, B279–35, ABC 2433 F	£800	£2500
Middle, Late Whaddon Chase		
V1485–1509, ABC 2445	£1700	£3500
BELGAE		
WONERSH		
M147, 148, V1522, B351–56, ABC 527	£1200	£3200
KENT		
WEALD NET		
M84, 229, V144, 150, B2466–68, ABC 177	£5000	£12500
NORFOLK		
ICENI		
Wolf type M49, a, b, V610, B212–278		
left facing	£650	£3000
right facing	£800	£2500
Freckenham Type I M397–399, 403b,		
V620, B3384–95, ABC 1432	£1300	£3800
Freckenham Type II M401, 2, 3a, 3c,		
V626, B3396–3419, ABC 1450	£1400	£3800
Snettisham Type M–, V–, B3353–83, ABC 1411	£1500	£3500
ATREBATIC (REMIC)		
M58–61, V210–216, B445–76, ABC 485	£900	£2600
SAVERNAKE FOREST		
M62, V1526, B359–64, ABC 2091	£500	£1500
DOBUNNIC		
M374, V1005, B2937–40, ABC 2003	£1200	£2500

ABOVE: Iceni Stater

■ **GOLD QUARTER STATERS WITHOUT LEGENDS**

	F	VF
AMBIANI		
Large flan type M2, 4, V15, 20, ABC 28 F	£600	£1500
Defaced die type M6, 8, V35, 37	£395	£950
GEOMETRIC		
M37, 39, 41, 41A, 42, V65, 146, 69, 67	£170	£475
KENT CANTII		
M40, 43–45, V143, 1225–1229	£500	£2000
VE MONOGRAM		
M83, V87 F	£400	£800
ATREBATIC		
M63–6, 69–75, V220–256, B478–546	£500	£2000
KENTISH		
Caesar's Trophy type V145	£400	£800
CORIELTAUVI		
Scyphate type M–, V–, B3187–93, ABC 1773	£400	£1000

■ **GOLD STATERS WITH LEGENDS**

	F	VF
COMMIUS		
M92, V350, B724–730, ABC 1022/25	£1300	£3500
TINCOMARUS		
M93, 94,93, V362, 363, B761–74		
Alfriston ABC 1049	£1500	£4000
Alton ABC 1052	£3000	£8000
Warrior ABC 1055–67	£1200	£2500
VERICA		
Equestrian type M121, V500,		
B1143–58, ABC 1190	£1200	£3400
Vine leaf type M125, V520, B1159–76,		
ABC 1193	£1600	£3500
EPATICCUS		
M262, V575, B2021–23, ABC 1343	£4000	£9500
CARATACUS		
Warrior		
CCI 20.0001 (this coin)	extra rare	£50000

DUBNOVELLANUS	F	VF
In Kent M283, V176, B2492–98, ABC303	£1200	£3100
In Essex M275, V1650, B2425–40, ABC 2392	£1600	£3000

EPPILLUS

In Kent M300–1, V430, B1125–28, ABC 384 & 387	£10000	30000

ADDEDOMAROS

M266, 7, V1605, B2390–94 F
Three types:

Floral Spiral ABC 2511	£2700	£4500
Crescent Cross ABC 2514	£1250	£2500
Spiral ABC 2517	£900	£2000

TASCIOVANUS

Bucranium M149, V1680, ABC 2553 B1591–1607 F	£4500	£6000
Equestrian M154–7, V1730–1736, B1608–13	£3500	£8000

TASCIO/RICON

M184, V1780, B1625–36, ABC 2580	£2500	£4900

SEGO

M194, V1845, B1625–27, ABC 441	£7500	£15000

ANDOCO

M197, V1860, B2011–14, ABC 2715	£3250	£8000

ABOVE: Tasciovanus 'Celtic Warrior' Stater

ABOVE: Cunobeline Stater

CUNOBELINUS

Biga type M201, V1910, B1769–71, ABC 2771	£3000	£9000

Corn ear M203 etc V2010, B1772–1835 F
Four types:

Linear ABC 2774	£2500	£6000
Plastic ABC 2789	£2000	£5000
Wild ABC 2783	£2000	£5000
Classic ABC 2798	£3000	£7000

DOBUNNI

ANTED of the Dobunni
M385–6, V1062–1066, B3023–27

ABC 2066 F	£1500	£4000

EISU	F	VF
M388, V1105, B3039–42 F	£2000	£4200

INAM

M390, V1140, B3056 F	£6000	£10000

CATTI

M391, V1130, B3057–60, ABC 2057 F	£1800	£4500

COMUX

M392, V1092, B3061–63, ABC 2054 F	£3000	£7000

CORIO

M393, V1035, B3064–3133, ABC 2048	£1600	£3200

BODVOC

M395, V1052, B3135–42, ABC 2309 F	£2400	£6500

ABOVE: Volisios Dumnocoveros Stater

ABOVE: Cunobeline Quarter Stater

CORIELTAVI
AVNT COST

ABC 1929; V.910; BMC 3258, ABC 1929	£1000	£2000

ESUPRASV

ABC 1917; V. 920; BMC 3269, ABC 1917	£900	£1900

VEP

ABC 1851; V.905; BMC3274–75, ABC 1851	£1000	£2400

VEP CORF

M549–460, V940, 930, B3296–3304, ABC 1854 F	£1900	£3800

DUMNOC TIGIR SENO

M461, V972, B3325–27, ABC 1971	£1400	£4100

VOLISIOS DUMNOCOVEROS

M463, V978, B3330–36	£485	£1625

VOLISIOS CARTIVEL Ext. rare	£8000	£12000

	F	VF
VA 933 LAT ISON ABC 1956	£5000	£10000

ICENI
| ECEN ABC 1651, V.725, BMC 4032 | £5000 | £14000 |

| ANTED | £4000 | £9000 |

ABOVE: Anted, silver Unit

■GOLD QUARTER STATERS WITH LEGENDS

TINCOMARUS
Tincom Commi M95, V365, ABC 1073	£800	£2000
Medusa head type M97, V378, B811–26, ABC 1076	£3000	£7000
Tablet type M101–4, V387–390, B825–79, ABC 1085	£550	£900

EPPILLUS
| Calleva M107, V407, B986–101, ABC 1148 | £900 | £2900 |

VERICA
| Horse type M111–114, V465–468, B1143–46, ABC 1199 | £500 | £1300 |

TASCIOVANUS
| Horse type M152–3, V1690, 1692, B1641–1650, ABC 2595 | £500 | £1100 |

CUNOBELINUS
| Various types, B1836–55, eg. ABC 2822 | £850 | £2100 |

■ SILVER COINS WITHOUT LEGENDS

DUROTRIGES
Silver Stater M317, V1235, B2525–2731, ABC 2157 F	£90	£300
Geometric type, Unit, M319, V1242, B2734–79 , ABC 2214	£50	£150
Starfish type, Unit, M320, V1270, B2780–81, ABC 2220	£65	£235

DOBUNNIC
| Face M374a, b, 5, 6, 8, V1020, B2950–3000, ABC 2012 | £700 | £4000 |
| Abstract M378a–384d, V1042, B3012–22, ABC 2027 | £70 | £300 |

CORIELTAUVI	F	VF
Boar type M405a, V855, B3194–3250, ABC 1779	£500	£1800
South Ferriby M410 etc, V875, ABC 1803	£200	£400

ICENI
Boar type M407–9, V655–659, B3440–3511, ABC 1582	£40	£350
Wreath type M414, 5, 440, V679, 675, B3763–74, ABC 1588	£50	£400
Face type M412–413e, V665, B3536–55, ABC1588	£50	£400

QUEEN BOUDICA (now refuted) NORFOLK GOD
| Face type M413, 413D, V790, 792, B3556–3759, ABC 1567 | £70 | £250 |

ATREBATES
COMMIUS
| Ladder–Head left M446b, V355, 357, B731–58, ABC 1040 | £190 | £400 |

■ SILVER COINS WITH LEGENDS

ATREBATES
EPPILLUS
| Calleva type M108, V415, B1016–1115, ABC 1160 | £100 | £390 |

EPATICCUS
| Eagle type M263, V580, B2024–2289, ABC 1346 | £150 | £200 |
| Victory type M263a, V581, B2294–2328, ABC 1349 | £155 | £250 |

VERICA
| Lion type M123, V505, B1332–59, ABC 1299 | £160 | £350 |

CARATACUS
| Eagle Type M265, V593, B2376–2384, ABC 1376 F | £185 | £585 |

CATUVELLANI
TASCIOVANUS
| Equestrian M158, V1745, B1667–68, ABC 2610 | £300 | £900 |
| VER type M161, V1699, B1670–73, ABC 2622 | £250 | £700 |

CUNOBELINE
| Equestrian M216–8, 6, V1951 1983, 2047, B1862, ABC 2861 | £300 | £800 |
| Bust right M236, VA2055, B1871–73, ABC 2873 | £200 | £700 |

DOBUNNI
ANTED of the Dobunni
| M387, V1082, B3032–38, ABC 1645 | £100 | £120 |

EISU EISU–OXO type
| M389, V1110, B3043–55, ABC 2081 | £90 | £200 |

	F	VF
BODVOC		
M396, V1057, B3143–45 ABC 2042 F	£200	£600
ECEN		
M424, V730, B4033–4215	£30	£85
ALE SCAVO, ABC 1705	£400	£1500
AESU		
M432, V775, B4558–72, ABC 1702	£80	£170
PRASUTAGUS		
King of the Iceni (husband of Boudica)		
B4577–4580, ABC 1711	£1000	£3500
CORIELTAUVI		
ESUPRASU		
M4566, VA924, B3272, ABC 1920	£100	£280
VEP CORF		
M460b, 464, V394, 950, B3277–3382,		
B3305–3314, ABC 1881	£65	£200
DUMNOC TIGIR SENO		
M462, V974, 980, B3339, ABC 1974	£300	£900
VOLISIOS DUMNOCOVEROS,		
ABC 1983	£400	£1100

■ **BRONZE, BASE METAL COINS WITHOUT LEGENDS**

	F	VF
POTIN		
Experimental type M22a, V104, ABC 144	£100	£300
Class I M9–22, V122–131, ABC 162	£80	£200
Class II M23–25, V136–139, ABC 171	£70	£150
Thurrock Types V1402–1442, ABC 126	£40	£150
ARMORICAN		
Billon stater, ABC 70	£70	£250
DUROTRIGES		
Bronze stater M318, V1290, ABC 2175	£25	£65
Cast type M332–370,		
V1322–1370, ABC 2196	£40	£120
TRINOVANTES		
NORTH THAMES		
M273, 274, 281,		
V1646, 1615, 1669, ABC 2541	£100	£250
CANTI		
NORTH KENT		
M295, 296, V154, ABC 267	£100	£400

■ **BRONZE COINS WITH LEGENDS**

	F	VF
DUBNOVELLANOS in Essex		
M277, 8, V1665, 1667, ABC 366	£80	£250

	F	VF
TASCIOVANUS		
Head, beard M168, 9, V1707, ABC 2658	£150	£300
TASCIOVANUS AT VERLAMIUM		
M172, V1808, ABC 2679	£100	£300
Boar, VER M179, V1713, ABC 2667	£100	£250
RUES Equestrian M190, V1892, ABC 2754	£110	£400
DIAS Centaur M192, V1882, ABC 2748	£150	£400
ANDOCO		
M200, V1871, ABC 2727	£250	£600
CUNOBELINE		
Victory, TASC M221, V1971, ABC 2924	£100	£300
Victory, CUN M22, a, V1973, ABC 2927	£120	£350
Winged animal, M225, V2081	£120	£350
Head, beard, M226, 9, V2131, 2085	£120	£350
Panel, sphinx, M230, V1977	£120	£350
Winged beast, M231, V1979	£120	£350
Centaur, M242, V2089	£120	£350
Sow, M243, V2091, ABC 2091	£150	£380
Warrior, M244, V2093	£150	£340
Boar, TASC, M245, V1983, ABC 2993	£150	£340
Metal worker, M248, V2097, ABC 2969	£180	£380
Horse, CAMV, M250, V2101, ABC 2975	£160	£350
Jupiter, horse, M251, V2103, ABC 2978	£160	£350
Janus head, M252, V2105, ABC 2981	£160	£350
Jupiter, lion, M253, V1207, ABC 2984	£150	£310
Sphinx, fig, M260, a, V2109, ABC 2987	£150	£400

CELTIC COINAGE

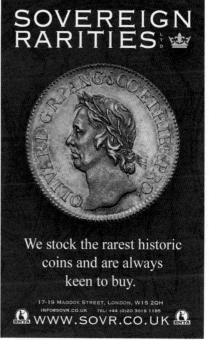

SOVEREIGN RARITIES LTD

We stock the rarest historic coins and are always keen to buy.

17-19 MADDOX STREET, LONDON, W1S 2QH
INFO@SOVR.CO.UK   TEL: +44 (0)20 3019 1185
WWW.SOVR.CO.UK

BRITISH COINS MARKET VALUES 2023 **53**

HAMMERED GOLD 1344–1662

Prices in this section are approximately what collectors can expect to pay for the commonest types of the coins listed. For most other types prices will range upwards from these amounts.

Precise valuations cannot be given since they vary from dealer to dealer and have to be determined by a number of factors such as a coin's condition, which is of prime importance in deciding its value.

For more detailed information, look at *English Hammered Coins, Volumes 1 and 2*, by J J North (Spink, 1994, 1992).

Serious collectors should also obtain *The Herbert Schneider Collection, Volume 1: English Gold Coins 1257–1603* (Spink, 1996) and *Volume 2: English Coins 1603–20th Century* (Spink, 2002).

■ THE PLANTAGENET KINGS

HENRY III 1216–1272	F	VF
Gold penny		£669000

One sold for £540000 (excluding buyer's premium) at auction in London in 2022

ABOVE: Edward III Treaty Quarter-noble

EDWARD III 1327–77
Third coinage
First period

		F	VF
Double-florins or Double Leopards		ext. rare	
Florins or leopards		ext. rare	
Half-florins or helms		£85000	*

Second period

		F	VF
Nobles	from	£52000	£135000
Half-nobles	from	£10000	£55000
Quarter-nobles	from	£3400	£10000

Third period

		F	VF
Nobles	from	£3400	£1000
Half-nobles	from	£3200	£9500
Quarter-nobles	from	£550	£1500

Fourth coinage
Pre-treaty period with France (before 1315)
With French title

	F	VF
Nobles	£1400	£3000
Half-nobles	£800	£2200
Quarter-nobles	£440	£750

Transitional treaty period, 1361
Aquitaine title added

	F	VF
Nobles	£1500	£3950
Half-nobles	£900	£2200
Quarter-nobles	£450	£900

ABOVE: Edward III Transitional Treaty Half-noble

Treaty period 1361–9
Omits FRANC

	F	VF
Nobles, London	£1500	£3300
Nobles, Calais (C in centre of reverse)	£1500	£3300
Half-nobles, London	£1000	£2250
Half-nobles, Calais	£1200	£3200
Quarter-nobles, London	£450	£800
Quarter-nobles, Calais	£450	£800

Post-treaty period 1369–77
French title resumed

	F	VF
Nobles, London	£1500	£4000
Nobles, Calais (flag at stern or C in centre)	£1500	£4000
Half-nobles, London	£3000	£6000
Half-nobles, Calais	£3000	£6000

There are many other issues and varieties in this reign. These prices relate to the commoner pieces.

ABOVE: Richard II Calais Noble

RICHARD II 1377–99

	F	VF
Nobles, London	£2250	£4500
Nobles, Calais (flag at stern)	£2250	£4500
Half-nobles, London	£2400	£5000
Half-nobles, Calais (flag at stern)	£2250	£5250
Quarter-nobles, London	£900	£2000

There are many different varieties and different styles of lettering.

ABOVE: Henry IV heavy coinage London Noble

ABOVE: Henry V annulet London Noble

HENRY IV 1399–1413	F	VF
Heavy coinage		
Nobles (120g) London	£9000	£22000
Nobles, Calais (flag at stern)	£10000	£25000
Half–nobles, London	£6500	*
Half–nobles, Calais	£8000	*
Quarter–nobles, London	£2300	£4500
Quarter–nobles, Calais	£2500	£6000
Light coinage		
Nobles (108g)	£2500	£6250
Half–nobles	£3000	£7750
Quarter–nobles	£800	£2300

HENRY VI 1422–61	F	VF
Annulet issue, 1422–27		
Nobles, London	£1500	£3500
Nobles, Calais (flag at stern)	£2000	£4000
Nobles, York	£2000	£5250
Half–nobles, London	£900	£2300
Half–nobles, Calais	£2400	£5250
Half–nobles, York	£2500	£5400
Quarter–nobles, London	£450	£700
Quarter–nobles, Calais	£450	£1100
Quarter–nobles, York	£450	£1100
Rosette–mascle issue 1427–30		
Nobles, London	£2500	£7200
Nobles, Calais	£3100	£8500
Half–nobles, London	£3200	£9000
Half–nobles, Calais	£4000	£12000
Quarter–nobles, London	£1250	£3300
Quarter–nobles, Calais	£3550	£3400

ABOVE: Henry V Noble

ABOVE: Henry VI rosette–mascle Calais Noble

HENRY V 1413–22		F	VF
Nobles, many varieties	from	£1800	£4500
Half–nobles		£1250	£3500
Quarter–nobles		£550	£950

This reign sees an increase in the use of privy marks to differentiate issues.

Pinecone–mascle issue 1430–4	F	VF
Nobles, London	£2500	£7200
Half–nobles, London	£4000	£12000
Quarter–nobles	£1300	£3800
Leaf–mascle issue 1434–5		
Nobles, London	£4750	£14500
Half–nobles, London	£4100	£12500
Quarter–nobles	£1300	£4250

Leaf–trefoil issue 1435–8

	F	VF
Nobles	£4000	£11000
Half-nobles	£4000	£12000
Quarter–noble	£1300	£4250

Trefoil issue 1438–43

	F	VF
Nobles	£4250	£11500

ABOVE: Henry VI Pinecone–mascle Noble

Leaf–pellet issue 1445–54

	F	VF
Nobles	£4750	£13500

Cross pellet issue 1454–60

	F	VF
Nobles	£5250	£16000

EDWARD IV 1st reign 1461–70
Heavy coinage 1461–65

	F	VF
Nobles (108g)	£8000	£20000
Quarter–noble	£2250	£6250

Light coinage 1464–70

	F	VF
Ryals or rose–nobles (120g) London	£1200	£2800
Flemish copy	£1000	£2000

Edward IV Light coinage Norwich Ryal

	F	VF
Ryals, Bristol (B in waves)	£1900	£5200
Ryals, Coventry (C in waves)	£2750	£7000
Ryals, Norwich (N in waves)	£2950	£7500
Ryals, York (E in waves)	£1600	£3800
Half-ryals, London	£900	£2250
Half-ryals, Bristol (B in waves)	£2500	£6500
Half-ryals, Coventry (C in waves)	£7000	£16000
Half-ryals, Norwich (N in waves)	£4500	£14500
Half-ryals, York (E in waves)	£1450	£3300
Quarter-ryals	£500	£1250
Angels	£17500	£50000

HENRY VI restored 1470–71

	F	VF
Angels, London	£2300	£5500
Angels, Bristol (B in waves)	£3750	£9250
Half-angels, London	£6700	£16000
Half-angels, Bristol (B in waves)	£8000	*

EDWARD IV 2nd reign 1471–83

	F	VF
Angels, London	£1000	£3000
Angels, Bristol (B in waves)	£6000	£12000
Half-angels, some varieties	£925	£2200

EDWARD IV or V 1483
im halved sun and rose

	F	VF
Angels	£7500	£16750
Half-angels	£7500	*

RICHARD III 1483–85

	F	VF
Angels, reading EDWARD, im boar's head on obverse, halved sun and rose on reverse	£11000	£28000
Angels, reading RICHARD or RICAD	£7000	£18250
Half-angels	£11000	*

ABOVE: Edward IV second reign Angel

■ THE TUDOR MONARCHS

HENRY VII 1485–1509

		F	VF
Sovereigns of 20 shillings (all extremely rare)	from	£30000	£95000
Ryals			ext. rare
Angels, varieties, different ims	from	£1350	£2750
Half-angels		£1100	£2200

ABOVE: Henry VIII Third coinage type I Sovereign

ABOVE: Henry VIII first coinage Angel, im portcullis

	F	VF
Angels	£1500	£3000
Half–angels	£1000	£2250
Quarter–angels	£900	£2550
Crowns, HENRIC 8, London	£900	£2500
Crowns, Southwark	£1000	£3000
Crowns, Bristol	£900	£2500
Halfcrowns, London	£750	£1800
Halfcrowns, Southwark	£800	£2000
Halfcrowns, Bristol	£900	£2800

EDWARD VI 1547–53
Posthumous coinage in the
name of Henry VIII, 1547–51

		F	VF
Sovereigns, London	from	£9750	£30000
Sovereigns, Bristol		£15000	£4000
Half–sovereigns, London		£11000	£3000
Half–sovereigns, Southwark		£1100	£3000
Crowns, London		£825	£2250
Crowns, Southwark		£900	£2750
Halfcrowns, London		£725	£2250
Halfcrowns, Southwark		£725	£2250

Coinage in Edward's own name
First period 1547–49

	F	VF
Half–sovereigns, Tower, reads EDWARD 6	£3500	£9000

HENRY VIII 1509–47

		F	VF
First coinage 1509–26			
Sovereigns of 20 shillings im			
crowned portcullis only		£14500	£40000
Ryal			ext. rare
Angels (6s 8d)	from	£1100	£2250
Half–angels		£800	£1900
Second coinage 1526–44			
Sovereigns of 22s 6d, various ims	from	£14500	£36000
Angels (7s 6d)	from	£1750	£5000
Half–angels im lis		£1400	£4750
George–nobles im rose		£17000	£37500
Half–George–noble		£16000	*
Crowns of the rose im rose		£16000	*
Crowns of the double rose			ext. rare
HK (Henry and Katherine of Aragon)		£1400	£3500
HA (Henry and Anne Boleyn)		£3750	£8500
HI (Henry and Jane Seymour)		£1400	£3500
HR (HENRICUS REX)		£1300	£3000
Halfcrowns of the double–rose			
HK		£800	£2500
HI		£1100	£2750
HR		£1200	£3200
Third coinage 1544–47			
Sovereigns of 20s, London	from	£8500	£23000
Sovereigns of 20s, Southwark		£8500	£23000
Sovereigns of 20s, Bristol	from	£15000	£42500
Half–sovereigns, London		£1500	£3750
Half–sovereigns, Southwark		£1500	£3750
Half–sovereigns, Bristol		£3000	£7500

ABOVE: Edward VI second period Sovereign im arrow

	F	VF
Half-sovereigns, Southwark	£2750	£7250
Crowns	£3900	£9000
Halfcrowns	£3000	£6250

Second period 1549–50

	F	VF
Sovereigns	£9250	£22500
Half-sovereign, uncrowned bust, London	£4750	£13250
Half-sovereigns, SCUTUM on obverse	£2500	£7750
Half-sovereigns, Durham House MDXLVII	£11000	*
Half-sovereigns, crowned bust, London	£2000	£7000
Half-sovereigns, half-length bust, Durham House	£10000	*
Crowns, uncrowned bust	£3000	£8500
Crowns, crowned bust	£2800	£7250
Halfcrowns, uncrowned bust	£2800	£7200
Halfcrowns, crowned bust	£2550	£6500

ABOVE: Mary 1553 Sovereign

PHILIP AND MARY 1554–8	F	VF
Angels, im lis	£8250	£22000
Half-angels	£16500	*

ABOVE: Edward VI third period Sovereign im tun

Third period 1550–53

	F	VF
'Fine' sovereigns of 30s, king enthroned	£55000	£140000
Sovereigns of 20s, half length figure	£8000	£21000
Half-sovereigns, similar to last	£3500	£7750
Crowns, similar but SCUTUM on reverse	£3350	£7500
Halfcrowns, similar	£2500	£7250
Angels	£20000	£45000
Half-angels	£19500	*

MARY 1553–4

	F	VF
Sovereigns, different dates, some undated, im pomegranate or half rose	£12500	£30000
Ryals, dated MDLIII (1553)	£49000	£10000
Angels, im pomegranate	£3500	£8000
Half-angels	£8750	*

ABOVE: Elizabeth I sixth issue Ryal

ELIZABETH I 1558–1603
Hammered issues

	F	VF
'Fine' Sovereigns of 30s, different issues from	£9000	£22000
Ryals	£22500	£61500
Angels, different issues	£1800	£4100
Half-angels	£1400	£3700
Quarter-angels	£1200	£3100

ABOVE: Elizabeth I second issue Quarter-angel

	F	VF		F	VF
Pounds of 20s, different ims from	£4750	£14000	Britain crowns	£450	£900
Half-pounds, different issues	£4000	£8250	Halfcrowns	£325	£675
Crowns	£2300	£6500	Thistle crowns, varieties	£375	£775
Halfcrowns	£1800	£4500			

ABOVE: Elizabeth I sixth issue Crown

Milled issues

	F	VF
Half-pounds, one issue but different marks	£6000	£13000
Crowns	£3500	£9500
Halfcrowns	£5250	£12500

■ THE STUART KINGS

ABOVE: James I third coinage Rose-ryal

ABOVE: James I third coinage Spur-ryal

ABOVE: James I third coinage Laurel

JAMES I 1603–25
First coinage 1603–4

	F	VF
Sovereigns of 20s, two busts	£4150	£12500
Half-sovereigns	£5200	£16500
Crowns	£3200	£8250
Halfcrowns	£1100	£3750

Second coinage 1604–19

	F	VF
Rose-ryals of 30s	£4500	£13000
Spur-ryals of 15s	£10500	£30000
Angels	£2300	£5750
Half-angels	£5150	£14000
Unites, different busts	£1300	£2500
Double crowns	£575	£1400

Third coinage 1619–25

	F	VF
Rose-ryals, varieties	£6000	£15000
Spur-ryals	£10500	£28000
Angels	£3250	£6750
Laurels, different busts	£1350	£2600
Half-laurels	£850	£1700
Quarter-laurels	£500	£900

CHARLES I 1625–49
Tower mint 1625–42
Initial marks: lis, cross-calvary, negro's head, castle, anchor, heart, plume, rose, harp, portcullis, bell, crown, tun, triangle, star, triangle-in-circle.

ABOVE: Charles I Tower mint Unite, im heart

	F	VF
Angels, varieties from	£6000	£13500
Angels, pierced as touchpieces	£1500	£3000
Unites	£1250	£2600
Double-crowns	£750	£1800
Crowns	£500	£825

ABOVE: Charles I Tower mint Double-crown, im heart

Tower mint under Parliament 1642-9
Ims: (P), (R), eye, sun, sceptre

Unites, varieties	£2150	£6250
Double-crowns	£1300	£3000
Crowns	£500	£1100

Briot's milled issues 1631-2
Ims: anemone and B, daisy and B, B

Angels	£11500	£42000
Unites	£5500	£14500
Double-crowns	£3800	£9000
Crowns	£5500	£15500

Briot's hammered issues 1638-9

Unite	£8500	*
Double-crowns	£4000	£9250
Crowns	£1500	£4100

Coins of provincial mints
Bristol 1645

Unites	ext. rare
Half-unites	ext. rare

Chester 1644

Unites	ext. rare

Exeter 1643-44

Unites	ext. rare

Oxford 1642-46

Triple unites	from	£25000	£45000
Unites	from	£5000	£11000
Half-unites	from	£3200	£7000

Truro 1642-43

	F	VF
Half-unites		ext. rare

Shrewsbury 1644

Triple unites and unites	ext. rare

Worcester 1643-44

Unites	ext. rare

ABOVE: Charles I 1643 Oxford Triple unite

Siege pieces 1645-49
Pontefract 1648-49

Unites F	ext. rare

ABOVE: Commonwealth 1651 Unite

COMMONWEALTH 1649-60

Unites im sun	£4000	£8000
im anchor	£10500	£23000
Double-crowns im sun	£3000	£6250
im anchor	£7000	£15500
Crowns, im sun	£1800	£4000
im anchor	£5500	£15500

ABOVE: Commonwealth 1650 Crown

CHARLES II 1660–85
Hammered Coinage 1660–62

ABOVE: Charles II hammered coinage Unite

		F	VF
Unites, two issues	from	£3250	£7250
Double–crowns		£1800	£4750
Crowns		£2100	£6150

HAMMERED SILVER

In this section, coins are mainly valued in Fine or Very Fine condition. Prices are based on coins of good metal that are not chipped or cracked.

However, pennies of the early Plantagenets, where higher-grade coins are seldom available, are valued in Fair or Fine condition.

Again it should be noted that prices are for the commonest types only, and are the amounts collectors can expect to pay, rather than dealers' buying prices.

Prices for the Saxon and Norman series are based on common mint towns. Rarer mints command higher premiums.

Descriptions such as 'cross/moneyer's name' indicate that a cross appears on the obverse and the moneyer's name on the reverse. For more details see *Standard Catalogue of British Coins* (Spink, annual), and *English Hammered Coins, volumes 1 and 2* by J J North, Spink (1991, 1994).

■ ANGLO–SAXON SCEATS AND STYCAS

ABOVE: Examples of Sceats

		F	VF
EARLY PERIOD c600–750			
Silver Sceats	from	£100	£295
Large numbers of types and varieties.			

		F	VF
NORTHUMBRIAN KINGS c737–867			
Silver Sceats c737–796	from	£185	£500
Copper Stycas c 810–867	from	£25	£75

Struck for many kings. Numerous moneyers and different varieties. The copper Styca is the commonest coin in the Anglo-Saxon series.

ARCHBISHOPS OF YORK c732–900			
Silver Sceats	from	£195	£500
Copper Stycas	from	£20	£60

■ KINGS OF KENT

HEABERHT c764		
Pennies monogram/cross		ext. rare
One moneyer (Eoba).		

ECGBERHT c765–780		F	VF
Pennies monogram/cross		£1850	£6250
Two moneyers (Babba and Udd).			

EADBERHT PRAEN 797–798		
Pennies EADBERHT REX/moneyer	£1750	£5500
Three moneyers.		

CUTHRED 789–807			
Pennies non-portrait, various designs from		£900	£3000
Bust right		£1250	£4250
Different moneyers and varieties.			

BALDRED c825		
Pennies bust right	£1850	£5950
Cross/cross	£1000	£3250
Different types and moneyers.		

ANONYMOUS		
Pennies bust right	£1500	£4750
Different types and moneyers.		

■ ARCHBISHOPS OF CANTERBURY

JAENBERHT 766–792			
Pennies various types non-portrait	from	£1200	£4750

AETHELHEARD 793–805			
Pennies various types			
non-portrait	from	£1200	£3850

WULFRED 805–832			
Pennies various groups			
portrait types	from	£1250	£4000

CEOLNOTH 833–870			
Pennies various groups, portrait types	from	£1500	£5000

AETHELRED		
Pennies, portrait	£3850	£12000
non portrait	£1500	£5250

PLEGMUND 890–914			
Pennies various types, non-portrait	from	£1000	£3250

ABOVE: step portrait Penny

■ KINGS OF MERCIA

OFFA 757–796			
Pennies non-portrait	from	£850	£2000
Portrait	from	£1650	£5000

CYNETHRYTH (wife of Offa)

		F	VF
Pennies portrait		£4650	£11000
Non-portrait		£1750	£5000

COENWULF 796–821

Pennies various types, portrait,		£1200	£3250
non-portrait	from	£725	£1850

ABOVE: Coenwulf portrait Penny

CEOLWULF 821–823

	F	VF
Pennies various types, portrait	£1850	£5750

BEORNWULF 823–825

	F	VF
Pennies various types, portrait	£1500	£5750

LUDICA 825–827

	F	VF
Pennies two types, portrait F	£9000	£28500

WIGLAF 827–829, 830–840

	F	VF
Pennies portrait	£5250	£16000
Non-portrait	£3000	£8500

BERHTWULF 840–852

	F	VF
Pennies portrait	£3000	£8500
non-portrait	£3750	£9500

BURGRED 852–874

	F	VF
Pennies one type portrait, five variants from	£375	£850

CEOLWULF II 874–c 877

	F	VF
Pennies two types portrait	£2850	£7000

KINGS OF EAST ANGLIA

BEONNA c758

	F	VF
Silver Sceat	£950	£3000

ALBERHT (749–?)

	F	VF
Penny, non-portrait type	£6000	£19500

AETHELBERHT died 794

	F	VF
Pennies, portrait type F	£7250	£23500

EADWALD c796

	F	VF
Pennies, non-portrait types	£1300	£4850

AETHELSTAN I c850

		F	VF
Pennies various types, portrait,	from	£1500	£5750
non-portrait,	from	£600	£1650

AETHELWEARD c 850

	F	VF
Pennies, non-portrait types	£1200	£4000

EADMUND 855–870

	F	VF
Pennies, non-portrait types	£525	£1350

■ VIKING INVADERS 878–954

ALFRED

Imitations of portrait, different types,

		F	VF
Pennies	from	£2850	£8500
Halfpennies	from	£1200	£4250

Non-portrait, different types,

Pennies	from	£775	£2250
Halfpennies	from	£925	£2500

Danish East Anglia, c885–954

AETHELSTAN II 878–890/1

	F	VF
Pennies cross/moneyer	£2000	£7500

OSWALD

	F	VF
Pennies A/cross	£3250	£10250

ST EADMUND

	F	VF
Pennies memorial coinage, various legends	£225	£525
Many moneyers.		
Halfpennies	£700	£2600
Many moneyers.		

ABOVE: St Eadmund memorial Penny

ST MARTIN OF LINCOLN c917

	F	VF
Pennies sword/cross	£4500	£14750

AETHELRED I c870

	F	VF
Pennies temple/cross	£2650	£7500

York
SIEVERT–SIEFRED–CNUT c897

		F	VF
Crosslet/small cross	from	£265	£625
Many different groups and varieties.			
Halfpennies		£895	£2650
Many different groups and varieties.			

EARL SIHTRIC unknown

	F	VF
Pennies non-portrait	£6000	£19500

REGNALD c 910

		F	VF
Pennies various types, some blundered	from	£3750	£12500

SIHTRIC I 921–926/7	F	VF
Pennies sword/cross	£3000	£10500

ANLAF GUTHFRITHSSON 939–941		
Pennies raven/cross	£3500	£8000
Cross/cross	£3250	£9500
Flower/cross	£5000	£16000

OLAF SIHTRICSSON 941–944, 948–952		
Pennies various types	£2850	£8250

SIHTRIC II c941–943		
Pennies shield/standard	£3500	£10000

REGNALD II c941–943		
Pennies cross/cross	£5250	£15000
Shield/standard	£5750	£16500

ERIC BLOODAXE 948, 952–954		
Pennies cross/moneyer	£8250	£27500
Sword/cross	£15000	£50000

ST PETER OF YORK c905–925			
Pennies various types	from	£450	£1475
Halfpennies, various types	from	£925	£3000

■ KINGS OF WESSEX

BEORHTRIC 786–802
Two types, non-portrait	ext. rare

ECGBERHT 802–839
Pennies four groups,		
portrait, non-portrait	£1500	£5500

Mints of Canterbury, London, Rochester, Winchester

AETHELWULF 839–858
Pennies four phases, portrait, non-portrait	£800	£2950

from mints of Canterbury, Rochester

AETHELBERHT 858–866
Pennies two types portrait	from	£1500	£3500

Many moneyers.

AETHELRED I 865–871
Pennies portrait types	from	£1000	£3500

Many moneyers.

ALFRED THE GREAT 871–899
Pennies portrait in style of Aethelred I	£1500	£4250
Four other portrait types, commonest		
has the London monogram reverse	£4500	£12500
Halfpennies	£1850	£5500
Pennies non-portrait types from	£800	£1750
Many different styles of lettering.		
Halfpennies	£875	£2500

EDWARD THE ELDER 899–924
Non-portrait types

	F	VF
Pennies cross/moneyer's name in two lines	£325	£750
Halfpennies cross/moneyer's name in two lines	£1850	£4250

ABOVE: Edward the Elder, non–portrait Penny

Portrait types
Pennies bust/moneyer's name	£1250	£3850
Many types, varieties and moneyers.		
Pennies design has buildings,		
floral designs and others	£3950	£10500
Many types, varieties and moneyers.		

■ KINGS OF ALL ENGLAND

AETHELSTAN 924–39
Non-portrait types
Pennies cross/moneyer's name in two lines	£395	£925
Cross/cross	£450	£1250
Halfpenny cross or floral lozenge/	£1950	£5250
Two lines		

Portrait types
Pennies bust/moneyer's name in two lines	£1500	£4750
Bust/small cross	£1200	£3850

Many other issues, some featuring buildings. There are also different mints and moneyer's names.

EADMUND 939–46
Non-portrait types
Pennies cross or rosette/moneyer's name in two lines	£375	£925
Halfpennies, cross or rosette/moneyer's name in two lines	£1250	£4000

Portrait types
Pennies crowned bust/small cross	£1250	£3950
Helmeted bust/cross crosslet	£1450	£5000

Many issues and varieties, different mint names and moneyers.

EADRED 946–55
Non-portrait types
Pennies cross/moneyer's name in two lines	£350	£800
Halfpennies cross/moneyer's name in two lines	£1250	£3250
Pennies rosette/moneyer's name	£500	£1650

Portrait types
Pennies crowned bust/small cross	£875	£3250

Many variations and mint names and moneyers.

HAMMERED SILVER

		F	VF
HOWEL DDA King of Wales, died c948			
Pennies small cross/moneyer's name in two lines (Gillys)			ext. rare
EADWIG 955–59			
Non-portrait types			
Pennies cross/moneyer's name	from	£800	£2500
Many variations, some rare.			
Halfpennies, non portrait types cross/moneyer's name		£1950	£4750
Portrait types			
Pennies bust/cross	from	£10000	£35000
EADGAR 959–75			
Non-portrait types			
Pennies cross/moneyer's name	from	£300	£750
Cross/cross from		£300	£750
Rosette/rosette from		£385	£875
Halfpennies	from	£1500	£5000

ABOVE: Eadgar, non-portrait Penny

	F	VF
Portrait types		
Pennies pre-reform, bust right	£1500	£4850
Halfpennies, diademed bust/London monogram	£1750	£4750
Pennies reform (c972), bust left	£1750	£5000
Many other varieties.		
EDWARD THE MARTYR 975–78		
Portrait types		
Pennies bust left/small cross	£2500	£6500
Many different mints and moneyers.		

AETHELRED II 978–1016

ABOVE: Aethelred II last small cross type Penny

		F	VF
Pennies first small cross type	from	£925	£2950
First hand type	from	£250	£525
Second hand type	from	£200	£485
Benediction hand type	from	£1500	£5000

</col>

		F	VF
CRUX type	from	£180	£375

ABOVE: Aethelred II CRUX type Penny

ABOVE: Aethelred II long cross type Penny

	F	VF
Long cross type	£180	£375
Helmet type	£195	£425
Last small cross type	£180	£375
Agnus Dei type	£12000	*

Other issues and varieties, many mints and moneyers.

		F	VF
CNUT 1016–35			
Pennies quatrefoil type	from	£175	£425

ABOVE: Cnut quatrefoil type Penny

		F	VF
Pointed helmet type	from	£165	£375

ABOVE: Cnut pointed helmet type Penny

		F	VF
Short cross type	from	£150	£365
Jewel cross type	from	£900	£2350

Other types, and many different mints and moneyers.

		F	VF
HAROLD I 1035–40			
Pennies Short cross type	from	£1500	£4250
Jewel cross type	from	£400	£1000
Long cross type with trefoils	from	£400	£1000
Long cross type with fleurs-de-lis		£350	£900

68 BRITISH COINS MARKET VALUES 2023

Many different mint names and moneyers.

HARTHACNUT 1035–42	F	VF
Pennies jewel cross type, bust left	£1650	£4250
Bust right	£1450	£4000
Arm and sceptre type	£1350	£3750

Different mint names and moneyers.

	F	VF
Pennies Scandinavian types struck at Lund	£600	£1450

EDWARD THE CONFESSOR 1042–66		
Pennies PACX type from	£260	£685
Radiate crown/small cross type	£185	£450
Trefoil quadrilateral type	£195	£425
Small flan type	£175	£400
Expanding cross type	£225	£500

ABOVE: Edward the Confessor transitional pyramids type Penny

Pointed helmet type	£245	£525
Sovereign/eagles type	£245	£525
Hammer cross type	£195	£425

ABOVE: Edward the Confessor hammer cross type Penny

Bust facing/small cross type	£185	£400
Pyramids type	£210	£525
Transitional pyramids type	£1950	£5250

Other issues, including a unique gold penny; many different mints and moneyers.

ABOVE: Harold II Pax type Penny, bust left, without sceptre

HAROLD II 1066
Pennies Pax type, crowned head left,

with sceptre	£1750	£4750

	F	VF
without sceptre	£2000	£5250

Pennies Pax type crowned head right,	F	VF
with sceptre	£4000	£10500

■ THE NORMAN KINGS

WILLIAM I 1066–87			
Pennies profile left/cross fleury type	from	£600	£1550
Bonnet type	from	£400	£1100
Canopy type	from	£600	£1650
Two sceptres type	from	£450	£1150
Two stars type	from	£425	£1000
Sword type	from	£600	£1500

ABOVE: William I profile/cross fleury type Penny

Profile right/cross and			
trefoils type	from	£685	£1975
PAXS type	from	£350	£675

WILLIAM II 1087–1100

ABOVE: William II cross voided type Penny

Pennies profile right type	from	£1000	£2950
Cross in quatrefoil type	from	£900	£2350
Cross voided type	from	£900	£2350
Cross pattée over fleury type	from	£925	£2500
Cross fleury and piles type	from	£975	£2650

ABOVE: Henry I large bust/cross and annulets type Penny

HENRY I 1100–1135

		F	VF
Pennies annulets type	from	£575	£1800
Profile/cross fleury type	from	£400	£1100
PAXS type	from	£365	£975
Annulets and piles type	from	£385	£1150
Voided cross and fleurs type	from	£850	£2850
Pointing bust and stars type	from	£1600	£5000
Facing bust/quatrefoil and piles type	from	£4755	£1350
Large profile/cross and annulets type	from	£1500	£4750
Facing bust/cross in quatrefoil type	from	£795	£2650
Full bust/cross fleury type		£475	£1250
Double inscription type		£685	£1850
Small profile/cross and annulets type		£525	£1400
Star in lozenge fleury type		£500	£1300
Pellets in quatrefoil type		£350	£825
Quadrilateral on cross fleury type		£285	£650
Halfpennies		£2500	£6500

STEPHEN 1135–54

		F	VF
Pennies cross moline (Watford) type	from	£295	£800

ABOVE: Stephen 'Watford' Penny

	F	VF
Similar, reads PERERIC	£875	£2850
Voided cross and mullets type	£365	£1100
Cross and piles type	£425	£1300
Cross pommée (Awbridge) type	£350	£1000

There are also a number of irregular issues produced during the civil war, all of which are very rare. These include several extremely rare and attractive pieces bearing the names of Empress Matilda and barons, such as Eustace Fitzjohn and Robert de Stuteville.

■ THE PLANTAGENET KINGS

HENRY II 1154–89

ABOVE: Henry II cross and crosslets (Tealby) Penny

		F	VF
Pennies cross and crosslets ('Tealby' coinage)		£150	£475

The issue is classified by bust variants into six groups, struck at 32 mints.

		F	VF
Pennies short cross from		£90	£250

The 'short cross' coinage was introduced in 1180 and continued through successive reigns until Henry III brought about a change in 1247. HENRICVS REX appears on all these coins but they can be classified into reigns by the styles of the busts and lettering. CR Wren's guide *The Short Cross Coinage 1180–1247* is the best book to identify coins of this series.

RICHARD I 1189–99

	F	VF
Pennies short cross	£100	£300

JOHN 1189–1216

	F	VF
Pennies short cross	£85	£225

ABOVE: John short cross Penny

HENRY III 1216–72

	F	VF
Pennies short cross	£40	£150
Long cross no sceptre	£35	£95
Long cross with sceptre	£30	£70

ABOVE: Henry III, long cross Penny with sceptre

The 'long cross' pennies, first introduced in 1247, are divided into two groups: those with sceptre and those without. They also fall into five basic classes, with many varieties. CR Wren's *The Voided Long Cross Coinage, 1247–79* is the best guide to identification.

ABOVE: Edward I, 1st coinage, long cross Penny

EDWARD I 1272–1307

		F	VF
1st coinage 1272–78			
Long cross pennies	from	£90	£200

Similar in style to those of Henry III but with more realistic beard.

New coinage 1278–1307			
Groats		£2700	£7500
Pennies, various classes, mints	from	£20	£65
Halfpennies	from	£35	£120
Farthings	from	£35	£120

ABOVE: Edward I Farthing London

The best guide to this era of coinage is *Edwardian English Silver Coins 1278–1351* (Sylloge of Coins of the British Isles no39).

EDWARD II 1307–27

		F	VF
Pennies, various classes, mints	from	£30	£85
Halfpennies	from	£65	£190
Farthing	from	£35	£120

EDWARD III 1327–77

1st and 2nd coinages 1327–43	F	VF
Pennies (only 1st coinage)		
various types and mints	£250	£750
Halfpennies, different types and mints	£25	£75
Farthings	£30	£80

3rd coinage 1344–51, florin coinage	F	VF
Pennies, various types and mints	£25	£95
Halfpennies	£25	£70
Farthings	£30	£100

ABOVE: Edward III, post–treaty Groat

4th coinage 1351–77		F	VF
Groats, many types and mints	from	£75	£200
Halfgroats		£40	£130
Pennies		£25	£90
Halfpennies, different types		£30	£125
Farthings, a few types		£125	£425

RICHARD II 1377–99

		F	VF
Groats, four types	from	£500	£1850

ABOVE: Richard II Groat

	F	VF
Halfgroats	£325	£825
Pennies, various types, London	£200	£575
York	£70	£250
Durham	£135	£475
Halfpennies, three main types	£35	£110
Farthings, some varieties	£120	£450

HENRY IV 1399–1413

		F	VF
Groats, varieties	from	£2500	£8750
Halfgroats		£1250	£3250
Pennies	from	£650	£1500
Halfpennies		£225	£725
Farthings		£875	£2650

ABOVE: Henry V Groat

HENRY V 1413–22

	F	VF
Groats, Type A	£1250	£3750
Groats, Type B	£425	£1250
Groats, Type C	£150	£585
Halfgroats, various types, from	£150	£485
Pennies, various types, from	£45	£145
Halfpennies, various types, from	£30	£120
Farthings, various types, from	£500	£1500

HENRY VI 1422–61

Annulet issue 1422–1427	F	VF
Different mints, from		
Groats	£70	£200
Halfgroats	£35	£135
Pennies	£35	£120
Halfpennies	£25	£70
Farthings	£200	£600

Annulet–Trefoil sub issue	F	VF
Groats	£75	£265

	F	VF
Halfgroats	£75	£200
Penny	£90	£300

Rosette-mascle issue 1427-1430

	F	VF
Groats	£80	£210
Halfgroats	£50	£160
Pennies	£40	£125
Halfpennies	£30	£95
Farthings	£225	£600

Pinecone-mascle issue 1430-1434

		F	VF
Groats	from	£80	£210
Halfgroats	from	£50	£150
Pennies		£40	£125
Halfpennies		£30	£95
Farthings		£200	£600

Leaf-mascle issue 1434-1435

		F	VF
Groats	from	£150	£400
Halfgroats		£175	£475
Pennies		£80	£225
Halfpennies		£35	£125

Leaf-trefoil issue 1435-1438

	F	VF
Groats	£90	£285
Halfgroats	£80	£265
Pennies	£100	£300
Halfpennies	£35	£100
Farthings	£350	£900

Trefoil issue 1438-1443

	F	VF
Groats	£90	£325
Halfgroats	£175	£500
Halfpennies	£30	£100
Penny	£500	£1500
Farthings	£300	£1100

Trefoil-pellet issue 1443-1445

	F	VF
Groats	£175	£525

ABOVE: Henry VI, leaf-mascle issue Groat

Leaf-pellet issue 1445-1454

	F	VF
Groats	£90	£275
Halfgroats	£100	£300
Pennies	£75	£225
Halfpennies	£30	£100
Farthings	£295	£875

Unmarked issue 1445-1454

	F	VF
Groats	£600	£1850
Halfgroats	£400	£1100

Cross-pellet issue 1454-1460

	F	VF
Groats	£165	£450
Halfgroats	£325	£975
Pennies	£80	£225
Halfpennies	£35	£100
Farthings	£295	£1000

Lis-pellet issue 1454-1460

	F	VF
Groats	£350	£875

There are many different varieties, initial marks and mints in this reign. These prices are for commonest prices in each issue.

EDWARD IV 1st Reign 1461-1470
Heavy coinage 1461-4

	F	VF
Groats, many classes, all London	£160	£485
Halfgroats, many classes, all London	£300	£1000
Pennies, different classes, London, York and Durham	£135	£385
Halfpennies, different classes, all London	£45	£140
Farthings, London	£495	£1300

ABOVE: Edward IV light coinage Groat

Light coinage 1464-70

		F	VF
Groats, many different issues, varieties, ims and mints	from	£85	£250
Halfgroats, ditto		£65	£200
Pennies, ditto		£45	£150
Halfpennies, ditto		£35	£110
Farthings, two issues	from	£475	£1350

ABOVE: Henry VI restored) Groat London

HENRY VI restored 1470–71		F	VF
Groats, different mints,			
different ims	from	£285	£750
Halfgroats	from	£295	£900
Pennies	from	£275	£800
Halfpennies	from	£200	£675

EDWARD IV 2nd reign 1471–83		F	VF
Groats, different varieties, mints	from	£80	£250
Halfgroats	from	£55	£165
Pennies	from	£40	£150
Halfpennies	from	£40	£130

EDWARD IV or V 1483	F	VF
im halved sun and rose		
Groats	£1650	£4750
Pennies	£1850	£5850
Halfpennies	£325	£925

ABOVE: Richard III Groat London

RICHARD III 1483–85	F	VF
Groats, reading EDWARD,		
initial mark boar's head on obverse,		
halved sun and rose on reverse	£1650	£4950
Groats, reading Ricard, London		
and York mints,		
various combinations of ims	£1100	£2750
Halfgroats	£1750	£5250
Pennies, York and Durham from	£450	£1100
London mint	£2000	£6000
Halfpennies	£325	£875
Farthing	£1650	£4250

PERKIN WARBECK, PRETENDER	F	VF
Groat, 1494	£3000	£6250

■ THE TUDOR MONARCHS

HENRY VII 1485–1509
Facing bust issues

ABOVE: Henry VII open crown type Groat London

		F	VF
Groats, all London			
Open crown without arches	from	£140	£450
Crown with two arches unjewelled		£120	£325
Crown with two jewelled arches		£90	£350
Similar but only one arch jewelled		£125	£400
Similar but tall thin lettering		£125	£400
Similar but single arch, tall thin lettering		£125	£400
Halfgroats, London			
Open crown without arches,			
tressure unbroken		£385	£1375
Double arched crown		£50	£195
Unarched crown		£50	£175
Some varieties and different ims.			
Halfgroats, Canterbury			
Open crown, without arches		£75	£245
Double arched crown			
Some varieties and different ims.		£75	£245
Halfgroats, York			
Double arched crown		£60	£185
Unarched crown with tressure broken		£65	£210
Double arched crown with keys			
at side of bust		£75	£245
Many varieties and different ims.			
Pennies, facing bust type			
London		£225	£800
Canterbury, open crown		£285	£850
Canterbury, arched crown		£125	£400
Durham, Bishop Sherwood, S on breast		£120	£400
York		£75	£245
Many varieties and ims.			
Pennies, 'sovereign enthroned' type			
London, many varieties		£65	£200
Durham, many varieties		£55	£175
York, many varieties		£50	£150
Halfpennies, London			
Open crown		£40	£140
Arched crown		£30	£90
Crown with lower arch		£25	£80
Some varieties and ims.			
Halfpennies, Canterbury			
Open crown		£70	£200
Arched crown		£60	£175
Halfpennies, York			
Arched crown and key below bust		£110	£325
Farthings, all London		£500	£1500

Profile issues	F	VF
Testoons im lis, three different legends	£22500	£45000
Groats, all London		
Tentative issue, double band to crown	£325	£11000

ABOVE: Henry VII regular issue Groat

	F	VF
Regular issue, triple band to crown	£160	£500
Some varieties and ims.		
Halfgroats		
London	£100	£350
London, no numeral after king's name	£500	£1400
Canterbury	£80	£295
York, two keys below shield	£75	£265
York, XB by shield	£250	£700

HENRY VIII 1509–47
First coinage 1509–26 with portrait of Henry VII

	F	VF
Groats, London	£165	£475
Tournai	£1350	£3850
Tournai, without portrait	ext. rare	
Halfgroats, London	£150	£500
Canterbury, varieties	£90	£325
York, varieties	£125	£350
Tournal	£950	£3250
Pennies, 'sovereign enthroned'		
type, London	£50	£165
Canterbury, varieties	£110	£300
Durham, varieties	£50	£150
Halfpennies, facing bust type,		
London	£35	£120
Canterbury	£80	£265
Farthings, portcullis type, London	£350	£900

ABOVE: Henry VIII second coinage Groat York

Second coinage 1526–44 with young portrait of Henry VIII

	F	VF
Groats, London, varieties, ims	£165	£550
Irish title, HIB REX	£385	£1100
York, varieties, ims	£185	£550
Halfgroats, London, varieties, ims	£85	£265
Irish title, HIB REX	£550	£1800
Canterbury, varieties, ims	£70	£220
York, varieties, ims	£75	£225

	F	VF
Pennies 'sovereign enthroned' type		
London, varieties, ims	£65	£165
Canterbury, varieties, ims	£165	£475
Durham	£45	£140
York	£500	£1425
Halfpennies, facing bust type		
London, varieties, ims	£40	£125
Canterbury	£35	£145
York, varieties, ims	£45	£150
Farthings, portcullis type	£385	£825

Third coinage 1544–47 and posthumous issues 1547–51 with old bearded portrait

	F	VF
Testoons or shillings		
London, Tower mint, varieties, ims from	£1300	£4750
Southwark, varieties, ims	£1300	£4750
Bristol, varieties, ims	£1450	£5500
Groats, six different busts, varieties, ims		
London, Tower mint	£175	£600
Southwark	£175	£600
Bristol	£175	£625
Canterbury	£175	£600
York	£175	£600
London, Durham House	£300	£925

ABOVE: Henry VIII third coinage Groat

	F	VF
Halfgroats, only one style of bust, except York which has two, varieties, ims		
London, Tower mint	£95	£375
Southwark	£125	£425
Bristol	£90	£300
Canterbury	£70	£250
York	£85	£325
London, Durham House	£485	£1850

ABOVE: Henry VIII third coinage Halfgroat Bristol

ABOVE: Henry VIII posthumous coinage Halfgroat Canterbury

	F	VF
Pennies, facing bust, varieties, ims		
London, Tower mint	£55	£210
Southwark	£95	£325
London, Durham House	£525	£1750
Bristol	£100	£320
Canterbury	£65	£185
York	£55	£165
Halfpennies, facing bust varieties, ims		
London, Tower mint	£80	£245
Bristol	£120	£300
Canterbury	£60	£185
York	£65	£170
Farthing	£950	£2875

EDWARD VI 1547–53
First period 1547–49
Shillings, London, Durham House,

im bow, patterns?		ext. rare
Groats, London, Tower, im arrow	£975	£4850
London, Southwark, im E, none	£950	£4500
Halfgroats, London, Tower, im arrow	£750	£2350
London, Southwark, im arrow, E	£700	£2000
Canterbury, im none	£500	£1575
Pennies, London, Tower, im	£550	£1750
London, Southwark, im E	£585	£1875
Bristol, im none	£550	£1750
Halfpennies, London, Tower im uncertain	£600	£1750
Bristol, im none	£700	£2150

ABOVE: Edward VI second period Shilling

Second period 1549–50
Shillings, London,

Tower various ims	£300	£1000
Bristol, im TC	£975	£4000
Canterbury, im T or t	£275	£1100
London (Durham House),		
im bow, varieties	£295	£1200

Third period 1550–53	F	VF
Base silver (similar to issues of second period)		
Shillings, London, Tower, im lis, lion, rose	£200	£975
Pennies, London, Tower, im escallop	£70	£235
York, im mullet	£70	£225
Halfpennies, London, Tower	£385	£1475
Fine silver issue		
Crown 1551 im Y, 1551–53 im tun	£1250	£3850

ABOVE: Edward VI 1551 Crown

Halfcrown, walking horse, 1551, im Y	£800	£2250
Galloping horse,		
1551–52, im tun	£800	£2500

ABOVE: Edward VI, fine silver issue Sixpence

1553, im tun	£1650	£4950
Shillings, im Y, tun	£165	£725
Sixpences, London (Tower), im y, tun	£165	£725
York, im mullet	£375	£1575
Threepences, London (Tower), im tun	£300	£1200
York, im mullet	£685	£2850
Pennies, sovereign type	£1250	£4850
Farthings, portcullis type	£1650	£5500

ABOVE: Mary Groat

MARY 1553–54	F	VF
Groats, im pomegranate	£250	£850
Halfgroats, similar	£850	£2750
Pennies, reverse VERITAS TEMP FILIA	£850	£2750
Reverse CIVITAS LONDON	£850	£2750

PHILIP AND MARY 1554–58		
Shillings, full titles, without date	£485	£1975
Full titles, without date also without XII £	500	£2150
Full titles, dated 1554	£500	£2150
Dated 1554, English titles only	£500	£2150
Dated 1555, English titles only	£500	£2150
Dated 1554, English titles		
only, also without XII	£575	£2250
Dated 1555, English titles		
only, also without XII	£800	*
Dated 1554 but date below bust	£5000	*
1555 but date below bust	£3950	*
1555 similar to previous		
but without ANG	£4250	*
Sixpences, full titles, 1554	£400	£1500
Full titles, undated		ext. rare
English titles, 1555	£450	£1650
Similar but date below bust, 1554	£1750	*
English titles, 1557	£425	£1750
Similar, but date below bust, 1557	£1850	*
Groats, im lis	£185	£650
Halfgroats, im lis	£750	£2500

ABOVE: Philip and Mary Halfgroat

Pennies, im lis	£525	£1850
Base pennies, without portrait	£75	£265

ELIZABETH I 1558–1603		
Hammered coinage, first issue 1558–61		
Shillings ELIZABETH		
Wire-line circles	£600	£2500
Beaded inner circles	£300	£1100
ET for Z	£150	£575

	F	VF
Groats		
Wire-line inner circles	£250	£725
Beaded inner circles	£110	£485
ET for Z	£75	£350
Halfgroats		
Wire-line inner circles	£350	£925
Beaded inner circles	£65	£225
Pennies		
Wire-line inner circles	£600	£2150
Beaded inner circles	£800	£3000
Countermarked shillings of Edward VI, 1560–61		
with portcullis mark		
(current for 4½d) F	£6000	*
with greyhound mark		
(current for 2½d) F	£7000	*

Hammered coinage, second issue 1561–82		
Sixpences, dated 1561–82	£85	£300
Threepences, 1561–82	£60	£165
Halfgroats, undated	75	£250
Threehalfpences, 1561–62,		
1564–70, 1572–79, 1581–82	£45	£185
Pennies, undated	£35	£120
Threefarthings, 1561–62, 1568,		
1572–78, 1581–82	£75	£285

ABOVE: Elizabeth I 1601 Crown

Hammered coinage, third issue 1583–1603		
Crowns, im 1	£1975	£4925

	F	VF
im 2	£4650	£12000
Halfcrowns, im 1	£1300	£2950
im 2 F	£3250	£11000
Shillings ELIZAB	£120	£500
Sixpences, 1582–1602	£60	£300
Halfgroats, E D G ROSA etc	£25	£80
Pennies	£30	£120
Halfpennies	£30	£100

There are many different initial marks, such as lis, bell or lion, featured on the hammered coins of Elizabeth I, and these marks enable collectors to date those coins which are not themselves dated. For more details see J J North's *English Hammered Coinage, Volume 2*.

ABOVE: Elizabeth I milled coinage 1561 Sixpence

Milled Coinage

		F	VF
Large size	from	£595	£3000
Intermediate		£450	£1375
Small		£375	£1000
1561		£195	£500
1562		£150	£500
1563–64, 1566		£130	£500
1567–68		£150	£500
1570–71		£400	£1200
Groats, undated		£160	£650
Threepences, 1561, 1562–64		£200	£700
Halfgroats		£275	£900
Threefarthings		£5000	*

■ THE STUART KINGS

JAMES I 1603–25
First coinage 1603–04

	F	VF
Crowns, reverse begins EXURGAT	£1500	£4250
Halfcrowns	£1750	£4850

	F	VF
Shillings, varieties	£120	£525

ABOVE: James I second coinage Shilling

	F	VF
Sixpences, dated 1603–04, varieties	£95	£350
Halfgroats, undated	£45	£135
Pennies	£35	£125

Second coinage 1604–19
Crowns reverse

	F	VF
begins QVAE DEVS	£1350	£3650
Halfcrowns	£1750	£5250
Shillings, varieties	£95	£400
Sixpences, dated 1604–15, varieties	£80	£275
Halfgroats, varieties	£30	£95
Pennies	£40	£100
Halfpennies	£40	£100

ABOVE: James I third coinage Shilling

Third coinage 1619–25

	F	VF
Crowns	£1100	£2250
Plume over reverse shield	£1350	£3650
Halfcrowns	£300	£975
Plume over reverse shield	£575	£1750
Shillings	£100	£375
Plume over reverse shield	£275	£900
Sixpences dated 1621–24	£75	£300
Halfgroats	£30	£80
Pennies	£30	£80
Halfpennies	£20	£70

CHARLES 1 1625–1649
Tower Mint 1625–1643
Crowns, obverse King on horseback, reverse shield
1st horseman/square shield im lis,

	F	VF
cross-calvary	£1100	£2950
Horseman/square shield, plume above shield im lis, cross-calvary, castle	£1950	£5750
2nd horseman/oval shield im plume, rose harp, some varieties from	£800	£2100
2nd horseman/oval shield, plume above shield, im plume, rose, harp	£1200	£3000
3rd horseman/round shield im bell, crown, tun, anchor, triangle, star, portcullis, triangle-in-circle, some varieties, from	£875	£2450
3rd horseman/round shield, plume above shield, im tun	£1000	£3250

Halfcrowns, obverse King on horseback, reverse shield

ABOVE: Charles I Tower mint Crown, plume on rev

	F	VF
im lis, cross-calvary	£750	£2850
Group B, 2nd bust/square shield im cross-calvary, negro's head, castle, anchor, heart, plume many varieties	£100	£395
Group B, 1st bust/square shield, plume above shield, im cross calvary, negro's head, castle, anchor, heart, plume	£1650	£4500
Group C, 3rd bust/oval shield im plume, rose	£95	£300
Group C, 3rd bust/oval shield, plume above im plume, rose	£200	£725
Group D 4th bust/oval or round shield im harp, portcullis, bell, crown, tun, many varieties from	£65	£250
Group D 4th bust/oval or round shield, plume above, im harp, portcullis, bell, crown, tun,	£700	£2650
Group E, 5th bust/square shield im tun, anchor, triangle, many varieties	£75	£275
Group F, 6th bust/square shield im anchor, triangle, star, triangle-in-circle, many varieties	£55	£195

Sixpences

	F	VF
1st bust/square shield, date above, 1625 im lis, cross-calvary, 1626 im cross-calvary	£125	£475
2nd bust/square shield, date above, 1625, 1626 im cross-calvary, 1626, 1627 im negro's head, 1628, 1629 im castle, 1629 im heart, 1630 im heart, plume	£160	£525
3rd bust/oval shield, im plume, rose,	£85	£325
3rd bust/oval shield, plume above, im plume, rose,	£125	£495
4th bust/oval or round shield, im harp, portcullis, bell, crown, tun	£65	£235

	F	VF
1st horseman/square shield im lis, cross-calvary, negro's head, castle, anchor, many varieties from	£325	£1250
1st horseman/square shield plume above shield im lis, cross-calvary, negro's head castle, anchor,	£700	£2650
2nd horseman/oval shield im plume, rose, harp, portcullis, many varieties from	£145	£425
2nd horseman/oval shield, plume above shield, im plume, rose, harp, portcullis	£365	£1000
3rd horseman/round shield im bell, crown, tun, portcullis, anchor, triangle, star many varieties from	£100	£325
3rd horseman/round shield plume above shield, im portcullis, bell, crown, tun,	£195	£600
4th horseman/round shield im star, triangle in circle	£85	£295

ABOVE: Charles I Tower mint Sixpence im crown

	F	VF
5th bust/square shield im tun, anchor, triangle, many varieties from	£65	£250
6th bust/square shield im triangle, star	£55	£200
Halfgroats, crowned rose both sides im lis, cross-calvary, negro's head	£30	£90
2nd bust/oval shield im plume, rose	£35	£100
2nd bus/oval shield, plume above, im plume	£45	£165
3rd bust/oval shield, plume above,	£30	£100
im rose, plume	£45	£165

ABOVE: Charles I Tower mint Halfcrown, im triangle

Shillings

	F	VF
Group A, 1st bust/square shield im lis, cross-calvary, some varieties	£150	£500
1st bust/square shield, plume above shield,		

	F	VF
4th bust/oval or round shield, im harp, crown, portcullis, bell, tun, anchor, triangle, star, many varieties from	£30	£90
5th bust/round shield, im anchor	£35	£110
Pennies, uncrowned rose both sides im one or two pellets, lis, negro's head	£30	£90
2nd bust/oval shield im plume	£30	£90
3rd bust/oval shield im plume, rose	£30	£90
4th bust/oval shield im harp, one or two pellets, portcullis, bell, triangle	£30	£90
5th bust/oval shield im one or two pellets, none	£30	£90
Halfpennies, uncrowned rose both sides im none	£20	£75

Tower Mint, under Parliament 1643–48
Crowns, obverse King on horseback, reverse shield

	F	VF
4th horseman/round shield im P, R, eye sun	£925	£2650
5th horseman/round shield im sun, sceptre	£1200	£3650

ABOVE: Charles I Parliament Shilling

Halfcrowns, obverse King on horseback, reverse shield

	F	VF
3rd horseman/round shield im P, R, eye sun	£50	£300
im P, foreshortened horse	£195	£625
5th tall horseman/round shield im sun, sceptre	£95	£325
Shillings, reverse all square shield		
6th bust, crude, im P, R, eye, sun	£50	£185
7th bust, tall, slim, im sun, sceptre	£80	£300
8th bust, shorter, older, im sceptre	£90	£350
Sixpences, reverse all square shields		
6th bust im P, R,	£75	£285
7th bust im P, R, eye, sun, sceptre	£65	£235
8th bust (crude style) im eye, sun	£125	£450
Halfgroats, 4th bust/round shield im P, R, eye sceptre	£30	£100
7th bust, old/round shield im eye, sun, sceptre	£25	£90
Pennies, 7th bust/oval shield im one or two pellets	£25	£80

ABOVE: Charles I Briot's issue Crown

Briot's first milled issue 1631–32, im flower and B

	F	VF
Crowns	£1850	£5250
Halfcrowns	£700	£2000
Shillings	£525	£1500
Sixpences	£210	£575
Halfgroats	£90	£250
Pennies	£90	£250

Briot's second milled issue 1638–39, im anchor and B, anchor and mullet

	F	VF
Halfcrowns	£750	£1850
Shillings	£275	£750
Sixpences	£125	£400

ABOVE: Briot's first milled issue Sixpence

Briot's hammered issue 1638–39, im anchor, triangle over anchor

	F	VF
Halfcrowns	£675	£1750
Shillings	£325	£925

ABOVE: Charles I 1645 Exeter Crown

		F	VF
Halfpounds		£1950	£5000
Crowns		£1475	£3950
Halfcrowns		£875	£3500
Shillings		£2250	£6500

Oxford 1642–46 im plume with band

		F	VF
Pounds, varieties	from	£4500	£13000
Halfpounds		£1800	£4350
Crowns		£1650	£4250
Halfcrowns		£350	£975
Shillings		£375	£1000
Sixpences		£325	£950
Groats		£250	£700
Threepences		£175	£500
Halfgroats		£140	£400
Pennies		£225	£675

Bristol 1643–45 im Bristol monogram, acorn, plumelet

		F	VF
Halfcrowns, varieties	from	£450	£1275

Provincial Mints

		F	VF
York 1642–44, im lion			
Halfcrowns, varieties	from	£385	£1200
Shillings		£250	£775
Sixpences		£325	£875
Threepences		£90	£260
Aberystwyth 1638–42 im open book			
Halfcrowns, varieties	from	£1500	£5500
Shillings		£625	£1750
Sixpences		£300	£950
Groats		£85	£240

Charles I Aberystwyth Groat

		F	VF
Threepences		£75	£210
Halfgroats		£70	£210
Pennies		£85	£300
Halfpennies		£300	£800
Aberystwyth–Furnace 1647–48, im crown			
Halfcrowns	from	£3000	£8000
Shillings		£5000	*
Sixpences		£1950	£4850
Groats		£285	£800
Threepences		£400	£1150
Halfgroats		£400	£1150
Pennies		£900	£3150
Shrewsbury 1642 im plume without band			
Pounds, varieties	from	£5250	£14500

ABOVE: Charles I York Shilling

	F	VF
Shillings	£500	£1475
Sixpences	£400	£1350
Groats	£265	£800
Threepences	£350	£950
Halfgroats	£350	£950
Pennies	£725	£1875

ABOVE: Charles I 1644 Bristol Halfcrown

		F	VF
LLate 'Declaration' issues 1645–6			
These bear the marks A, B and plume.			
Ashby de la Zouch mint, 1645			
Halfcrowns, varieties	from	£4750	*
Shillings, varieties		£2000	£6000
Sixpences, varieties		£1650	£5250
Groats, varieties		£1475	£4500
Threepences, varieties		£900	£2850
Bridgnorth–on–Severn, 1646			
Halfcrowns, varieties	from	£1750	£6000
Shillings, varieties		£900	£2750
Sixpences, varieties		£300	£925
Groats, varieties		£265	£700
Threepence, varieties		£250	£625
Halfgroats, varieties		£625	£1650
Truro 1642–43 im rose, bugle			
Crowns, varieties	from	£600	£1425
Halfcrowns		£1250	£3750
Shillings		£5750	*

ABOVE: Charles I 1646 Bridgnorth-on-Severn Halfcrown

Exeter 1643–46 im Ex, rose, castle		F	VF
Halfpounds			ext. rare
Crowns, varieties	from	£500	£1425
Halfcrowns		£485	£975
Shillings		£575	£1750
Sixpences		£375	£1100
Groats		£175	£525
Threepences		£165	£425
Halfgroats		£300	£800
Pennies		£400	£1000
Worcester 1644–5 im castle, helmet, leopard's head, lion, two lions, lis, rose, star			
Halfcrowns, many varieties	from	£950	£4750
Salopia (Shrewsbury) 1644 im helmet, lis, rose in legend			
Halfcrowns, many varieties	from	£1500	£5500

Worcester or Salopia (Shrewsbury) 1643–4 im bird, boar's head, lis, castle, cross and annulets, helmet, lion, lis, pear, rose, scroll

		F	VF
Shillings, varieties	from	£2200	£6000
Sixpences		£1850	£5000
Groats		£675	£2000
Threepences		£425	£975
Halfgroats		£475	£1200
'HC' mint (probably Hartlebury Castle, Worcester, 1646) im pear, three pears			
Halfcrowns		£1650	£6000
Chester 1644 im cinquefoil, plume, prostrate gerb, three gerbs			
Halfcrowns, varieties	from	£1375	£3950
Shillings		£3500	£10000
Threepences		£1200	£3750
Welsh Marches mint? 1644			
Halfcrowns		£1850	£5750
Carlisle besieged 1644–45			
Three shillings		£13500	£30000
Shillings F		£9750	£21500
Newark besieged 1645–6, surrendered May 1646			
Halfcrowns, F		£1100	£2500

ABOVE: Charles I 1645 Newark Halfcrown

		F	VF
Shillings, 1645–46, varieties F		£900	£1950
Ninepences, 1645–46		£800	£1625
Sixpences		£900	£1850
Pontefract besieged 1648–49			
Two shillings, 1648		£8000	£25000
Shillings, 1648, varieties		£2750	£6000

ABOVE: Charles I 1648 Pontefract Shilling

Scarborough besieged 1644–45
Many odd values issued were issued in Scarborough, all of which are extremely rare. The coin's value was decided by the intrinsic value of the piece of metal from which it was made.
Examples: 5s 8d, 2s 4d, 1s 9d, 1s 3d, 7d F
Collectors can expect to pay at least £25000 or more in F and £40000 in VF for any of these.

COMMONWEALTH 1649–60

	F	VF
Crowns, im sun 1649, 51–54, 56	£1500	£3950
Halfcrowns, im sun 1649, 1651–6	£400	£975
im anchor 1658–60	£1875	£4000
Shillings, im sun 1649, 1661–87	£350	£750
im anchor 1658–60	£1200	£2750
Sixpences, im sun 1649, 1651–7	£275	£625
im anchor 1658–6	£800	£1850
Halfgroats undated	£45	£110
Pennies undated	£40	£100
Halfpennies	£40	£100

CHARLES II 1660–85
Hammered coinage 1660–62
First issue

		F	VF
Halfcrown	from	£1600	£5750
Shilling		£525	£1650
Sixpence		£300	£1150
Twopence		£50	£125
Penny		£30	£110

ABOVE: Charles II hammered first issue Shilling

Second issue

		F	VF
Halfcrown		£1250	£5500
Shilling		£700	£2450
Sixpence		£1375	£4000
Twopence	from	£25	£90
Penny		£30	£80

Third issue

	F	VF
Halfcrown	£200	£650
Shilling	£165	£550
Sixpence	£125	£450
Fourpence	£35	£120
Threepence	£20	£80
Twopence	£20	£65
Penny	£20	£70

'ROYAL' AND 'ROSE' BASE METAL FARTHINGS

Until 1613 English coins were struck only in gold or silver, because the monarchy thought base metal would diminish the royal prerogative of coining.

However silver coins became far too small and farthings so tiny that they had to be discontinued.

So to meet demands for small change, James I authorised Lord Harington to issue copper farthing tokens.

Subsequently this authority passed in turn to the Duke of Lennox, the Duchess of Richmond and Lord Maltravers.

It ceased by order of Parliament in 1644.

■ ROYAL FARTHING TOKENS

	Fair	F	VF	EF
JAMES II				
Type 1				
Harington, c1613. Larger flan with tin-washed surface, mint-mark between sceptres below crown	£18	£35	£95	£385
Type 2				
Harington, c1613. Larger flan, no tin wash	£18	£23	£55	£180
Type 3				
Lennox, 1614–25. IACO starts at 1 o'clock position	£12	£18	£45	£150
Type 4				
Lennox, 1622–25. Oval flan, IACO starts at 7 o'clock	£18	£35	£95	£310

	Fair	F	VF	EF
CHARLES I				
Type 1				
Richmond, 1625–34 single arched crown	£12	£20	£45	£110
Type 2				
Transitional, c1634 double arched crown	£12	£28	£75	£270
Type 3				
Maltravers, 1634–36 inner circles	£12	£22	£45	£130
Type 4				
Richmond, 1625–34 as Type 1 but oval	£15	£35	£80	£305
Type 5				
Maltravers, 1634–36 double arched crown	£18	£40	£85	£230

■ ROSE FARTHING TOKENS

These have a rose on the reverse.

	Fair	F	VF	EF
Type 1				
Small thick flan	£12	£20	£40	£150
Type 2				
Small thick flan, but single arched crown	£10	£18	£35	£110
Type 3				
Small thick flan, but sceptres below crown	£18	£40	£75	£170

ABOVE: From left to right: James I Harington farthings, types 1, 2 and 3

ABOVE: From left to right: Charles I Richmond, Maltravers and rose farthings

GUERNSEY STAMPS
AND COLLECTABLES

£5 Banknote

The Guernsey £5 note was introduced at the end of the Second World War and is dominantly pink. It features Queen Elizabeth II and illustrations of The Town Church in St Peter Port, which dates back to the 11th century. The back of the note features Fort Grey, nicknamed the 'cup and saucer' – a Martello tower built on a rock in the parish of St Peter. Along with an illustration of Hanois Lighthouse, built between 1860 and 1862 to help prevent shipwrecks off the Island's western coast. Contact the bureau for more information

Guernsey Uncirculated Coins

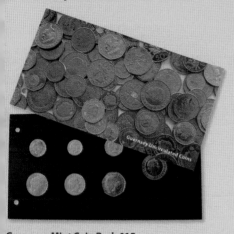

Guernsey Mint Coin Pack £15

A set of seven Guernsey coins are supplied in a Presentation Pack containing design information and specifications. Coins included are: £2, 50p, 20p, 10p, 5p, 2p, 1p.

Around the World in 80 days 50p collection

Five British Isles 50p coins have been released, issued to celebrate the 150th Anniversary of Jules Verne's epic adventure story; Around the World in 80 Days. This global novel has been translated into hundreds of languages, adapted into numerous films and TV shows and even inspired multiple real-life imitations. This stunning set – released by Guernsey Treasury and officially approved by Her Majesty the Queen – features FIVE coins each struck to superior Brilliant Uncirculated Quality.

MILLED COINAGE FROM 1656

This listing gives a general indication of value throughout the entire milled series. It is a guide for collectors only, not dealers' buying prices. The prices are a reasonable assessment of the market at the time of compilation, and for strictly graded coins, pieces of exceptional quality can sell for considerably more. Standards of grading also vary, so always seek advice if you are unsure, contact the British Numismatic Trade Association.

Prices are drawn from auction results and dealers' lists, with the aim of determining firm valuations, but prices still vary enormously from sale to sale and from one dealer's list to another. For practical reasons, only some of the varieties, dates and errors are mentioned.

The silver and base metal coinage up to the beginning of the reign of George III is graded to extremely fine, afterwards they are graded up to uncirculated. The condition, or grade, of a coin is of great importance in determining its value.

For further assistance see the sections on grading (pp44–45), abbreviations and terms (pp46–47).

For practical reasons we have ceased cataloguing coins produced beyond 2010, so please refer to the Royal Mint website.

◼ CROMWELL GOLD PATTERNS

These were struck by order of Cromwell, with the consent of the Council of State.

Thomas Simon made the dies, and the coins were struck on Peter Blondeau's machine.

The fifty shillings and the broad were struck from the same dies, but the fifty shillings has the edge inscription PROTECTOR LITERIS LITERAE NUMMIS CORONA ER SALUS, while the broad is not as thick and has a grained edge.

No original strikings of the half–broad are known, but some were struck from dies made by Joh)n Tanner in 1738.

All three denominations are dated 1656.

	F	VF	EF	Unc
Fifty shillings	*	£80000	£245000	*
Broad	*	£15000	£32500	£55000
Half–broad	*	*	£30000	*

ABOVE: Oliver Cromwell gold Broad 1656

◼ FIVE GUINEAS

CHARLES II	F	VF	EF	Unc
1668–78 pointed end of trnctn of bust	£6500	£13500	£55000	*
1668, 69, 75 as above, eleph below bust	£6500	£13500	£55000	*
1675–8 as above, eleph & castle below bust	£6500	£13500	£55000	*
1678–84 rounded end to trnctn	£6500	£13500	£55000	*
1680–4 as above, eleph & castle	£6500	£13500	£55000	*

ABOVE: Charles II 1670 proof Five Guineas

JAMES II				
1686 sceptres in wrong order on rev	£6500	£12500	£57000	*
1687–8 sceptres correct	£6500	£12500	£57000	*
1687–8 eleph & castle	£6500	£12500	£57000	*

WILLIAM AND MARY				
1691–4 no prov mark	£6000	£12000	£50000	*
1691–4 eleph & castle	£6000	£12500	£53000	*

ABOVE: William and Mary 1692 elephant & castle Five Guineas

WILLIAM III	F	VF	EF	Unc
1699–1700 no				
prov mark	£5500	£11000	£45000	*
1699 eleph & castle	£5500	£11250	£47500	*
1701 new bust				
'fine work'	£5500	£11000	£40000	*

ANNE

Pre-Union with Scotland

	F	VF	EF	Unc
1703 VIGO below bust	*	£220000	£525000	*
1705–6 plain below	£8000	£16000	£55000	*

Post-Union with Scotland

	F	VF	EF	Unc
1706	£7500	£13500	£50000	*
1709 larger lettering				
wider shield and				
crowns	£6500	£13500	£50000	*
1711, 1713–4				
broader bust	£6500	£12000	£45000	*

The pre–Union reverse has separate shields, top and right, for England and Scotland, while post–Union reverses have the English and Scottish arms side by side on the top and bottom shields.

GEORGE I

	F	VF	EF	Unc
1716, 17, 20, 26	£7000	£13000	£65000	*

ABOVE: George I 1716 Five Guineas

GEORGE II

	F	VF	EF	Unc
1729, 31, 35,				
38, 41 YH	£4500	£7000	£30000	*
1729 YH,				
E.I.C. below head	£4500	£7000	£30000	*
1746 OH, LIMA				
below	£4500	£7000	£30000	*
1748, 53 OH				
plain below	£4500	£7000	£30000	*

GEORGE III

	F	VF	EF	Unc
1770, 73, 77 patterns only	*	*	£170000	£375000

■ TWO GUINEAS

CHARLES II	F	VF	EF	Unc
1664, 65, 69, 71 pointed				
end to trnctn	£2500	£5000	£24000	*
1664 elephant below	£2500	£5000	£24000	*
1675–84 rounded end				
to trnctn	£2500	£5000	£20000	*
1676, 78, 82–84				
eleph & castle				
below bust	£2500	£5000	£20000	*
1678 eleph below				ext. rare

JAMES II	F	VF	EF	Unc
1687	£2750	£6000	£25000	*
1688/7	£2750	£6000	£25000	*

WILLIAM AND MARY	F	VF	EF	Unc
1691, 93, 94 eleph				
& castle	£2850	£5700	£20000	*
1693, 94 no				
prov mark	£2850	£5900	£20000	*

WILLIAM III	F	VF	EF	Unc
1701	£3000	£5500	£20000	*

ANNE	F	VF	EF	Unc
1709, 11, 13, 14	£2500	£4000	£15000	*

GEORGE I	F	VF	EF	Unc
1717, 20, 26	£2250	£4500	£15000	£35000

GEORGE II	F	VF	EF	Unc
1734, 35, 38, 39, YH F	£1500	£2000	£5000	£10000
1739–40 IH	£1500	£2000	£5000	*
1748, 53, OH	£1600	£2200	£5500	*

GEORGE III	F	VF	EF	Unc
1768, 73, 77 patterns only	*	*	£60000	£12000

■ BROAD

CHARLES II	F	VF	EF	Unc
1662	£2500	£3750	£12000	*

■ GUINEAS

CHARLES II	F	VF	EF	Unc
1663 pointed trnctn	£3500	*	*	*
1663 eleph	£2750	£7500	*	*
1664 trnctn				
indented	£3000	£8000	*	*
1664 eleph	£2750	£8500	*	*
1664–73 sloping pointed				
trnctn	£1200	£3250	£13000	*
1664, 65, 68 eleph	£1400	£4500	£2000	*
1672–84 rounded trnctn	£1000	£2800	£1000	*
1674–84 eleph & castle	£1300	£3000	£11000	*
1677–8 eleph				ext. rare

ABOVE: Charles II 1663 Guinea, elephant below bust

JAMES II	F	VF	EF	Unc
1685–6 1st bust	£900	£3000	£9500	*
1685 1st bust eleph & castle	£1000	£3500	£11500	*
1686–8 2nd bust	£900	£2500	£9000	*
1686–8 2nd bust eleph & castle	£1100	£3200	£11000	*

WILLIAM AND MARY				
1689–94 no prov mark	£1000	£3000	£9500	*
1689–94 eleph & castle	£1100	£3250	£10500	*
1692 eleph	£1500	£3500	£11500	*

WILLIAM III				
1695–6 1st bust	£750	£1800	£6000	*
1695, 6 eleph & castle	£750	£1800	£6000	*
1697–1701 2nd bust	£750	£1900	£6250	*
1697–1701 eleph & castle	£1500	£5500	*	*
1701 3rd bust 'fine work'	£1000	£2750	£9500	*

ANNE				
Pre–Union				
1702, 1705–07 plain below bust	£1100	£3500	£13000	*
1703 VIGO below	£102000	£30000	£80000	*

Post–Union				
1707–8 1st bust	£900	£2000	£6250	*
1707 eleph & castle	£1100	£3000	£8000	*
1707–9 2nd bust	£750	£1700	£5000	£9000
1708–9 eleph & castle	£1100	£3500	*	*
1710–1714 3rd bust	£700	£1200	£4500	£8000

Pre–Union reverse has separate shields, top and right, for England and Scotland. Post–Union reverses have the English and Scottish arms side by side on both the top and bottom shields.

GEORGE I				
1714 1st hd PR. EL. (Prince Elector) in rev legend	£1500	£4000	£13000	£30000
1715 2nd hd, tie with two ends	£800	£1750	£5500	£8000

	F	VF	EF	Unc
1715–16 3rd hd, hair not curling round trnctn	£800	£1750	£5500	£8000
1716–23 4th hd, tie with loop	£800	£1600	£4750	£7500
1721–2 eleph & castle	*			ext. rare
1723–7 5th hd, smaller, older bust	£650	£1400	£4500	£6500
1726 eleph & castle	£2000	£7000	*	*

GEORGE II				
1727 1st YH, small lettering	£1100	£3000	£9750	*
1727–28 1st YH larger lettering	£1200	£3500	£10000	*
1729–32 2nd YH	£900	£2800	£7500	*
1729, 31–32 E.I.C. below	£925	£3000	£8750	*
1732–38 larger lettering	£700	£1600	£4500	£7000
1732 E.I.C. below	£950	£3000	£8000	*
1739–40, 43 intermediate hd	£700	£1400	£4000	£7000
1739 E.I.C. below	£950	£3000	£8750	*
1745–6 larger lettering	£625	£1500	£4000	£7000
1746 LIMA below	£3250	£6500	£18000	*
1746–53, 55–56, 58–59, 60, OH	£550	£1100	£4000	£6000

GEORGE III				
1761 1st hd	£1500	£3500	£1000	£16000
1763–64 2nd hd	£1500	£3500	£7750	*
1765–73 3rd hd	£660	£825	£2500	£5000
1774–79, 81–86 4th hd	£475	£675	£1500	£2850
1789–99 5th hd, 'spade' rev F	£475	£675	£1000	£1600
1813 6th hd, rev shield in Garter ('Military guinea')	£900	£1650	£4500	£7500

ABOVE: George II 1760 Guinea

ABOVE: George III 1813 Guinea

■ HALF–GUINEAS

CHARLES II	F	VF	EF	Unc
1669–72 bust with pointed trnctn	£700	£1700	£6000	*
1672–84 rounded truncation	£700	£1700	£6000	*
1676–78, 80, 82, 84 eleph & castle	£800	£1900	£7500	*

JAMES II				
1686–88 no prov mark	£600	£1700	£5500	£10000
1686 eleph & castle	£2500	*	*	*

WILLIAM AND MARY				
1689 1st busts	£700	£1900	£6000	*
1690–4 2nd busts	£750	£1950	£6000	*
1691–2 eleph & castle	£800	£2000	£6000	*
1692 eleph	£1600	*	*	*

ABOVE: William and Mary 1689 Half-guinea

WILLIAM III				
1695 no prov mark	£500	£1000	£4000	£6500
1695–6 eleph & castle	£700	£1600	£5550	*
1697–1701 larger harp on rev	£500	£1000	£4000	£6500
1698 eleph & castle	£650	£1700	£6000	*

ANNE Pre–Union				
1702, 05 plain below bust	£800	£2850	£8000	£14000
1703 VIGO below	£7000	£17000	£42500	*

Post–Union				
1707–1714 plain	£500	£800	£2500	£6250

Pre-Union reverse has separate shields, top and right, for England and Scotland. Post-Union reverses have the English and Scottish arms side by side on the top and bottom shields.

GEORGE I				
1715, 17–24 1st hd	£400	£750	£2900	£4500
1721 eleph & castle	*	*	*	ext. rare
1725–27 smaller older hd	£350	£650	£2750	£4000

GEORGE II				
1728–39 YH	£475	£1000	£3750	*

	F	VF	EF	Unc
1729–32, 39 E.I.C. below	£575	£1400	£5000	*
1740, 43, 45–46 intermediate hd	£425	£800	£3000	*
1745 LIMA below	£1550	£3250	£10000	*
1747–53, 55–56, 58–60 OH	£375	£600	£1900	£3500

ABOVE: George II 1756 Half-guinea

GEORGE III				
1762–63 1st hd	£600	£1800	£4500	*
1764–66, 68–69, 72–75 2nd hd	£300	£575	£1700	*
1774–75 3rd hd	£900	£2000	£6250	*
1775–79, 81, 83–86 4th hd	£325	£475	£1100	£2250
1787–91, 93–98, 1800 5th hd	£275	£375	£1000	£1850
1801–03 6th hd	£275	£375	£1000	£1600
1804, 06, 08–11, 13 7th hd	£275	£375	£800	£1500

■ THIRD–GUINEAS

GEORGE III				
1797–1800 1st hd	£150	£200	£550	£900
1801–03 date close to crown on rev	£150	£200	£550	£900
1804–05, 08–11 2nd hd	£150	£200	£550	£900

■ QUARTER–GUINEAS

GEORGE I				
1718	£150	£300	£600	£1100

GEORGE III				
1762	£175	£350	£650	£1200

ABOVE: George III 1762 Quarter-guinea

■ FIVE POUNDS

GEORGE III				
1820 pattern F	*	*	*	£400000

	F	VF	EF	Unc
GEORGE IV				
1826 proof	*	*	£2500	£65000
VICTORIA				
1839 proof, 'Una and				
the Lion' rev F	*	*	£11000	£260000

ABOVE: Victoria 1839 proof Five Pound with 'Una and the Lion'

	F	VF	EF	Unc
1887 JH F	£1850	£2000	£3000	£4000
1887 proof	*	*	£5000	£17000
1887 proof no B.P.	*	*	£6500	£20000
1893 OH F	£1850	£2200	£3900	£6250
1893 proof	*	*	£7500	£23000
EDWARD VII				
1902 F	£1850	£1950	£2750	£4000
1902 proof	*	*	£2750	£4000
GEORGE V				
1911 proof F	*	*	*	£14000
GEORGE VI				
1937 proof	*	*	*	£7500

In 1984 the Royal Mint issued the first of an annual issue of Brilliant Uncirculated £5 coins.

These bear the symbol 'U' in a circle to the left of the date on the reverse to indicate the standard of striking.

BV indicates bullion value. At the time of going to press gold is approximately £1050 per troy oz.

ELIZABETH II Sovereign Issues	Unc
1953 proof	ext. rare
1980 proof, originally issued in Royal Mint set	BV
1981 proof	BV
1982 proof, originally issued in Royal Mint set	BV
1984 proof	BV
	Unc
1984 BU	BV
1985 proof	BV
1985 BU	BV

	F	VF	EF	Unc
1986 BU				BV
1987 new effigy, BU				BV
1988 BU				BV
1989 proof, 500th anniversary of the sovereign,				
originally issued in Royal Mint set				£2500
1989 BU, 500th anniversary of the sovereign				BV
1990 proof, originally issued in Royal Mint set				BV
1990 BU				BV
1991 proof, originally issued in Royal Mint set				BV
1991 BU				BV
1992 proof, originally issued in Royal Mint set				BV
1992 BU				BV
1993 proof, originally issued in Royal Mint set				BV
1993 BU				BV
1994 proof, originally issued in Royal Mint set				BV
1994 BU				BV
1995 proof, originally issued in Royal Mint set				BV
1995 BU				BV
1996 proof, originally issued in Royal Mint set				BV
1996 BU				BV
1997 proof, originally issued in Royal Mint set				BV
1997 BU				BV
1998 proof, originally issued in Royal Mint set				BV
1998 BU				BV
1999 proof, originally issued in Royal Mint set				BV
1999 BU				BV
2000 proof, originally issued in Royal Mint set				BV
2000 BU				BV
2001 proof, originally issued in Royal Mint set				BV
2001 BU				BV
2002 shield reverse, proof,				
originally issued in Royal Mint set				BV
2002 BU				BV
2003 proof, originally issued in Royal Mint set				BV
2003 BU				BV
2004 proof, originally issued in Royal Mint set				BV
2004 BU				BV
2005 proof, originally issued in Royal Mint set				BV
2005 BU				BV
2006 proof, originally issued in Royal Mint set				BV
2006 BU				BV
2007 proof, originally issued in Royal Mint set				BV
2008 proof, originally issued in				
Royal Mint four coin set				BV
2009 proof, Countdown to London 2012				BV
2009 proof, Henry VIII				BV
2009 BU				BV
2010 proof				BV
2011 proof				BV
2011 BU				BV
2012 proof				BV
2012 BU				BV
2013 proof				BV
2013 BU				BV
2014 proof				BV
2014 BU				BV
2015 proof				BV
2015 proof, new portrait				BV
2015 BU				BV

2016 proof, Butler portrait .... BV
2016 BU .... BV

ABOVE: George IV 1823 Two pounds

■ TWO POUNDS

GEORGE III	F	VF	EF	Unc
1820 pattern F	*	*	£26500	£66000
GEORGE IV				
1823 St George on rev F	*	£850	£2500	£5250
1826 proof, shield rev	*	*	£6250	£15000
WILLIAM IV				
1831 proof	*	*	£7500	£22500
VICTORIA				
1887 JH F	£750	£850	£1100	£1700
1887 proof	*	*	£1800	£3250
1893 OH F	£775	£900	£1800	£3250
1893 proof	*	*	£2750	£6250
EDWARD VII				
1902 F	£750	£850	£1200	£2400
1902 proof	*	*	£1200	£2400
GEORGE V				
1911 proof F	*	*	*	£3750
GEORGE VI				
1937 proof	*	*	*	£3250

ELIZABETH II	Unc
1953 proof	ext. rare
1980 proof, originally issued in Royal Mint set	BV
1982 proof, originally issued in Royal Mint set	BV
1983 proof	BV
1985 proof, originally issued in Royal Mint set	BV
1987 proof	BV
1988 proof	BV
1989 500th anniversary of the sovereign, proof	£1250
1990 proof	BV
1991 proof	BV
1992 proof	BV
1993 proof	BV
1996 proof	BV
1998 proof, originally issued in Royal Mint set	BV
2000 proof, originally issued in Royal Mint set	BV

2002 shield rev, proof, originally issued in Royal Mint set	BV
2003 proof, originally issued in Royal Mint set	BV
2004 proof, originally issued in Royal Mint set	BV
2005 proof, originally issued in Royal Mint set	BV
2006 proof, originally issued in Royal Mint set	BV
2007 proof, originally issued in Royal Mint set	BV
2008 proof, originally issued in Royal Mint set	BV
2009 proof, originally issued in Royal Mint set	BV
2010 proof	BV
2011 proof	BV
2012 proof	BV
2012 BU	BV
2013 proof	BV
2013 BU	BV
2014 proof	BV
2014 BU	BV
2015 proof	BV
2015 proof, new portait	BV
2016 proof, Butler portait	BV

■ SOVEREIGNS

ABOVE: George III 1817 Sovereign

Early sovereigns can attain considerably higher prices if flawless

GEORGE III	F	VF	EF	Unc
1817 F	£550	£800	£2250	£4500
1818	£850	£1750	£4750	£9500
1819	£36000	£57000	*	*
1820	£550	£700	£1900	£3500
GEORGE IV				
Type Laureate head/St George				
1821 F	£500	£700	£1500	£3500
1821 proof	*	*	£4000	£12000
1822 F	£500	£700	£1500	£3700
1823	£950	£2250	£6500	£12000
1824	£500	£700	£1900	£5250
1825	£675	£1650	£4750	£10000
Type bare head/shield				
1825 F	£500	£700	£1500	£3500
1826	£500	£700	£1500	£3500
1826 proof	*	*	£3750	£12000
1827 F	£500	£700	£1500	£3500
1828 F	£4500	£11000	£27000	*
1829	£500	£700	£1500	£3750
1830	£500	£725	£1700	£3800
WILLIAM IV				
1831	£550	£925	£2400	£5000

	F	VF	EF	Unc
1831 proof	*	*	£4250	£13000
1832 F	£500	£800	£1800	£3500
1833	£500	£800	£1850	£4200
1835	£500	£800	£2100	£4400
1836	£500	£800	£2200	£4000
1837	£500	£850	£2400	£4500

ABOVE: William IV 1833 Sovereign

VICTORIA
Type 1, YH/shield

	F	VF	EF	Unc
1838	£750	£1400	£3250	£7000
1838 wreath leaves different	£2500	£5500	£22000	*
1839	£1200	£1900	£45000	£11000
1839 proof	*	*	£5500	£14000
1841	£4750	£8500	£14000	£27000
1842	*	*	£600	£2000
1843	*	*	£600	£2000
1843 narrow shield	£3200	£6500	£17000	*
1844	*	*	£600	£2000
1845	*	*	£750	£2200
1846	*	*	£750	£2200
1847	*	*	£500	£1400
1848	*	*	£500	£1250
1849	*	*	£750	£3000
1850	*	*	£425	£1350
1851	*	*	£425	£1350
1852	*	*	£425	£1350
1853	*	*	£425	£1350
1853 proof	*	*	£9000	£25000
1854	*	*	£425	£1500
1855	*	*	£425	£1500
1856	*	*	£425	£1500
1857	*	*	£425	£1500
1858	*	*	£425	£1500
1859	*	*	£425	£1500
1859 'Ansell'	£750	£2750	£7000	*
1860	*	*	£425	£1850
1861	*	*	£425	£1000
1862	*	*	£425	£1000

ABOVE: Victoria 1859 'Ansell' Sovereign

	F	VF	EF	Unc
1863	*	*	£400	£800
1863 '827' on trnctn	£5250	£8750	*	*
1863 die number below wreath on rev	*	*	£400	£900
1863 '827' on trnctn	£4500	£7500	£15000	*
1864 die no	*	*	£400	£950
1865 die no	*	*	£400	£950
1866 die no	*	*	£400	£950
1868 die no	*	*	£400	£950
1869 die no	*	*	£400	£950
1870 die no	*	*	£400	£950
1871 die no	*	*	£400	£950
1871 S (Sydney mint) below wreath	*	*	£380	£725
1872	*	*	£380	£475
1872 die no	*	*	£380	£475
1872 M (Melbourne mint) below wreath	*	*	£380	£840
1872 S	*	*	£380	£1050
1873 die no	*	*	£380	£475
1873 S	*	*	£380	£1050
1874 die no	£1800	£3800	£9000	*
1874 M	*	*	£380	£750
1875 S	*	*	£380	£1050
1877 S	*	*	£380	£1050
1878 S	*	*	£380	£900
1879 S	*	*	£380	£800
1880 M	£625	£1150	£4250	*
1880 S	*	*	£380	£1000
1881 M	*	*	£550	£6500
1881 S	*	*	£450	£1250
1882 M	*	*	£425	£925
1882 S	*	*	£500	£1500
1883 M	*	£450	£1250	£2400
1883 S	*	*	£380	£800
1884 M	*	*	£380	£725
1884 S	*	*	£300	£925
1885 M	*	*	£380	£700
1885 S	*	*	£380	£700
1886 M	£1450	£3200	£6250	£12000
1886 S	*	*	£425	£1750
1887 M	£900	£1900	£5300	£10000
1887 S	*	*	£500	£1500

ABOVE: Victoria 1871 St George Sovereign

Type II, YH/St George and dragon

	F	VF	EF	Unc
1871	*	*	£380	£600
1871 S below hd	*	*	£500	£1850
1872	*	*	£380	£600

	F	VF	EF	Unc
1872 M below hd	*	*	£750	£3500
1872 S	*	*	£380	£975
1873	*	*	£375	£575
1873 M	*	*	£395	*
1873 S	*	*	£475	£2400
1874	*	*	£380	£575
1874 M	*	*	£380	£1400
1874 S	*	*	£380	£1400
1875 M	*	*	£380	£900
1875 S	*	*	£400	£925
1876	*	*	£380	£625
1876 M	*	*	£380	£900
1876 S	*	*	£380	£900
1877 M	*	*	£380	£900
1878	*	*	£380	£600
1878 M	*	*	£380	£900
1879	£550	£1400	£4250	*
1879 M	*	*	£400	£925
1879 S	*	*	£900	£3000
1880	*	*	£380	£575
1880 M	*	*	£425	£800
1880 S	*	*	£425	£800
1881 M	*	*	£550	£1200
1881 S	*	*	£425	£800
1882 M	*	*	£425	£800
1882 S	*	*	£425	£700
1883 M	*	*	£400	£650
1883 S	*	*	£400	£600
1884	*	*	£380	£550
1884 M	*	*	£400	£600
1884 S	*	*	£400	£600
1885	*	*	£380	£550
1885 M	*	*	£400	£700
1885 S	*	*	£380	£625
1886 M	*	*	£380	£975
1886 S	*	*	£380	£625
1887 M	*	*	£380	£725
1887 S	*	*	£380	£800

ABOVE: Victoria 1887 Jubilee Head Sovereign

Jubilee head coinage

	F	VF	EF	Unc
1887 F	*	*	£380	£500
1887 proof	*	*	£900	£3500
1887 M (Melbourne mint)	*	*	£380	£700
1887 S (Sydney mint)	*	*	£600	£2400
1888	*	*	£380	£450
1888 M	*	*	£380	£625
1888 S	*	*	£395	£825
1889	*	*	£380	£475
1889 M	*	*	£380	£525

	F	VF	EF	Unc
1889 S	*	*	£380	£525
1890	*	*	£380	£450
1890 M	*	*	£380	£650
1890 S	*	*	£380	£900
1891	*	*	£380	£500
1891 M	*	*	£380	£525
1891 S	*	*	£380	£525
1892	*	*	£380	£475
1892 M	*	*	£380	£500
1892 S	*	*	£380	£500
1893 M	*	*	£380	£500
1893 S	*	*	£380	£500

Old head coinage

	F	VF	EF	Unc
1893	*	*	£375	£450
1893 proof	*	*	£1300	£3500
1893 M	*	*	£375	£575
1893 S	*	*	£375	£475
1894	*	*	£375	£450
1894 M	*	*	£375	£475
1894 S	*	*	£375	£475
1895	*	*	£375	£450
1895 M	*	*	£375	£475
1895 S	*	*	£375	£475
1896	*	*	£375	£450
1896 M	*	*	£375	£475
1896 S	*	*	£375	£475
1897 M	*	*	£375	£475
1897 S	*	*	£374	£475
1898	*	*	£375	£450
1898 M	*	*	£375	£475
1898 S	*	*	£375	£475
1899	*	*	£375	£450
1899 M	*	*	£375	£475
1899 P (Perth mint)	*	*	£500	£1500
1899 S	*	*	£375	£475
1900	*	*	£375	£450
1900 M	*	*	£375	£450
1900 P	*	*	£375	£450
1900 S	*	*	£375	£475
1901	*	*	£375	£425
1901 M	*	*	£375	£475
1901 P	*	*	£375	£475
1901 S	*	*	£375	£475

EDWARD VII

	F	VF	EF	Unc
1902	*	*	*	£380
1902 proof	*	*	£400	£700
1902 M	*	*	*	£390
1902 P	*	*	*	£390
1902 S	*	*	*	£390
1903	*	*	*	£390
1903 M	*	*	*	£390
1903 P	*	*	*	£390
1903 S	*	*	*	£350
1904	*	*	*	£380
1904 M	*	*	*	£390
1904 P	*	*	*	£390
1904 S	*	*	*	£390

	F	VF	EF	Unc		F	VF	EF	Unc
1905	*	*	*	£385	1916 S	*	*	*	£385
1905 M	*	*	*	£385	1917 F	*	£5000	£11000	£17000
1905 P	*	*	*	£390	1917 C	*	*	£370	£425
1905 S	*	*	*	£390	1917 M	*	*	*	£385
1906	*	*	*	£390	1917 P	*	*	*	£385
1906 M	*	*	*	£390	1917 S	*	*	*	£385
1906 P	*	*	*	£390	1918 C	*	*	£370	£395
1906 S	*	*	*	£390	1918 I	*	*	£370	£450
1907	*	*	*	£390	1918 M	*	*	*	£450
1907 M	*	*	*	£390	1918 P	*	*	*	£385
1907 P	*	*	*	£390	1918 S	*	*	*	£385
1907 S	*	*	*	£390	1919 C	*	*	£375	£450
1908	*	*	*	£390	1919 M	*	*	*	£525
1908 C on ground					1919 P	*	*	*	£525
below dragon F	*	*	£6000	£11000	1919 S	*	*	*	£525
1908 M	*	*	*	£390	1920 M	£950	£2100	£3850	£6000
1908 P	*	*	*	£390	1920 P	*	*	*	£380
1908 S	*	*	*	£390	1920 S			highest	rarity
1909	*	*	*	£390	1921 M	£3200	£5400	£9500	£17500
1909 C	*	£400	£525	£1750	1921 P	*	*	*	£385
1909 M	*	*	*	£390	1921 S	*	£700	£1150	£2500
1909 P	*	*	*	£390	1922 M	£3200	£5250	£8000	£12000
1909 S	*	*	*	£390	1922 P	*	*	*	£385
1910	*	*	*	£390	1922 S	£5200	£8750	£13000	£18500
1910 C	*	£380	£450	£1250	1923 M	*	*	*	£390
1910 M	*	*	*	£390	1923 S	£2600	£4200	£7500	£14000
1910 P	*	*	*	£390	1923 SA (Pretoria Mint)	£3100	£4200	£8500	*
1910 S	*	*	*	£390	1923 SA proof	*	*	*	£3500
					1924 M	*	*	*	£385
					1924 P	*	*	*	£385
GEORGE V					1924 S	*	£625	£1400	£2400
1911	*	*	*	£390	1924 SA	*	*	£8000	*
1911 proof	*	*	*	£2000	1925	*	*	*	£385
1911 C	*	*	*	£385	1925 M	*	*	*	£385
1911 M	*	*	*	£385	1925 P	*	*	*	£400
1911 P	*	*	*	£385	1925 S	*	*	*	£385
1911 S	*	*	*	£385	1925 SA	*	*	*	£385
1912	*	*	*	£385	1926 M	*	*	*	£385
1912 M	*	*	*	£385	1926 P	*	£425	£800	£1200
1912 P	*	*	*	£385	1926 S	£5000	£8500	£14000	*
1912 S	*	*	*	£385	1926 SA	*	*	*	£385
1913	*	*	*	£385	1927 P	*	*	£375	£550
1913 C F	£385	£490	£1600	*	1927 SA	*	*	*	£385
1913 M	*	*	*	£385	1928 M	£600	£850	£1800	£3500
1913 P	*	*	*	£385	1928 P	*	*	*	£385
1913 S	*	*	*	£385	1928 SA	*	*	*	£385
1914	*	*	*	£385	1929 M	*	£725	£1900	£4000
1914 C	*	£380	£425	£850	1929 P	*	*	*	£385
1914 M	*	*	*	£385	1929 SA	*	*	*	£385
1914 P	*	*	*	£385	1930 M	*	*	£365	£425
1914 S	*	*	*	£385	1930 P	*	*	£365	£435
1915	*	*	*	£385	1930 SA	*	*	*	£380
1915 M	*	*	*	£385	1931 M	*	*	£395	£850
1915 P	*	*	*	£425	1931 P	*	*	*	£385
1915 S	*	*	*	£385	1931 SA	*	*	*	£385
1916	*	*	*	£450	1932	*	*	*	£385
1916 C F	*	£8000	£13500	£20000					
1916 M	*	*	*	£385	**GEORGE VI**				
1916 P	*	*	*	£385	1937 proof only	*	*	*	£3000

ABOVE: George VI 1937 proof Sovereign

ELIZABETH II	F	VF	EF	Unc
1953 proof	*	*	*	£385000
One sold at Baldwins in 2014 for £396,000 including premium				
1957	*	*	*	£375
1958	*	*	*	£375
1959	*	*	*	£375
1962	*	*	*	£375
1963	*	*	*	£375
1964	*	*	*	£375
1965	*	*	*	£375
1966	*	*	*	£375
1967	*	*	*	£375
1968	*	*	*	£375
1974	*	*	*	£375
1976	*	*	*	£375
1976 proof			*	ext. rare
1977	*	*	*	£375
1978	*	*	*	£375
1979	*	*	*	£375
1979 proof				£395
1980	*	*	*	£375
1980 proof				£395
1981	*	*	*	£375
1981 proof				£395
1982	*	*	*	£375
1982 proof				£375
1983 proof				£395
1984 proof				£395
1985 proof				£395
1986 proof				£395
1987 proof				£395
1988 proof				£395
1989 500th anniversary of sovereign, proof				£1250
1990 proof				£395
1991 proof				£395
1992 proof				£395
1993 proof				£395
1994 proof				£395
1995 proof				£395
1996 proof				£395
1997 proof				£395
1998 proof				£395
1999 proof				£395
2000 proof				£380
2000 BU				£360
2001 proof				£380
2001 BU				BV
2002 shield, proof				£450
2002 BU				BV
2003 proof				£380

	F	VF	EF	Unc
2003 BU				BV
2004 Proof				£380
2004 BU				BV
2005 proof				£380
2005 BU				BV
2006 proof				£380
2006 BU				BV
2007 proof				£380
2007 BU				BV
2008 BU				BV
2008 proof				£380
2009 BU				BV
2009 proof				£380
2010 proof				£380
2010 BU				BV
2011 proof				£380
2011 BU				BV
2012 proof				£380
2012 BU				BV
2013 proof				£380
2013 BU				BV
2013 BU "I" mint mark				BV
2014 proof				£380
2014 BU				BV
2015 proof				£380
2015 BU				BV
2015 proof, new portrait				£380
2016 proof				£380
2016 BU				BV
2017 proof				£400
2017 BU				BV
2018 proof				£400
2018 BU				BV
2019 proof				£400
2019 BU				BV

■ HALF–SOVEREIGNS

GEORGE III	F	VF	EF	Unc
1817	£225	£350	£700	£1800
1818	£250	£3275	£800	£1950
1820	£200	£275	£700	£1800

GEORGE IV	F	VF	EF	Unc
Laureate hd/ornate shield date				
1821	£700	£1100	£2850	£6000
1821 proof	*	*	£3750	£8250
1823 plain shield	£225	£375	£950	£2000
1824	£225	£375	£925	£1950
1825	£225	£375	£925	£1800
Bare hd, date/shield and full legend				
1826	£225	£350	£900	£1800
1826 proof	*	*	£1800	£5500
1827	£235	£375	£950	£2000
1828	£225	£375	£950	£2000

WILLIAM IV	F	VF	EF	Unc
1831 proof	*	*	£2500	£5500

	F	VF	EF	Unc
1834 reduced size	£300	£525	£1300	£2850
1835 normal size	£250	£450	£1000	£2000
1836 sixpence obv die	£1400	£3200	£7500	*
1836	£250	£475	£1100	£2400
1837	£250	£475	£1100	£2400
VICTORIA				
1838	*	£200	£700	£1450
1839 proof only	*	*	£1750	£3500
1841	*	£200	£750	£1650
1842	*	£200	£575	£1200
1843	*	£200	£675	£1350
1844	*	£200	£575	£1200
1845	£300	£600	£2750	*
1846	*	£200	£575	£1200
1847	*	£200	£575	£1200
1848	*	£200	£575	£1200
1849	*	£200	£575	£1200
1850	£225	£425	£1550	*
1851	*	£200	£525	£1000
1852	*	£200	£575	£1100
1853	*	£200	£500	£975
1853 proof	*	*	£4500	£12000
1855	*	£200	£550	£950
1856	*	£200	£575	£1200
1857	*	£200	£575	£1200
1858	*	£200	£575	£1200
1859	*	£200	£400	£925
1860	*	£200	£450	£750
1861	*	£200	£450	£750
1862	£1200	£3250	£7500	*
1863	*	£200	£550	£850
1863 die no	*	£200	£425	£900
1864 die no	*	£200	£425	£850
1865 die no	*	£200	£425	£850
1866 die no	*	£200	£425	£850
1867 die no	*	£200	£425	£850
1869 die no	*	£200	£425	£850
1870 die no	*	£200	£400	£725
1871 die no	*	£200	£425	£850
1871 S below shield	£190	£400	£1600	£4250
1872 die no	*	£200	£400	£700
1872 S	£190	£225	£1100	£3750
1873 die no	*	£200	£400	£700
1873 M below shield	£190	£225	£1100	£3700
1874 die no	*	£200	£400	£700
1875 die no	*	£200	£400	£700
1875 S	£190	£275	£1600	*
1876 die no	*	£190	£360	£625
1877 die no	*	£190	£360	£625
1877 M	£190	£300	£2000	£8250
1878 die no	*	£190	£400	£525
1879 die no	*	£190	£350	£525
1879 S	£190	£275	£1600	*
1880	*	£190	£400	£725
1880 die no	*	£200	£500	*
1880 S	£190	£240	£1400	*
1881 S	£225	£525	*	*
1881 M	£325	£550	*	*

	F	VF	EF	Unc
1882 S	£275	£650	£3700	*
1882 M	£180	£300	£1200	*
1883	*	£185	£350	£525
1883 S	£185	£300	£1200	*
1884	*	£190	£350	£600
1884 M	£185	£350	£1650	*
1885	*	£190	£350	£600
1885 M	£185	£285	£1500	£4500
1886 S	£185	£325	£1400	£4700
1886 M	£225	£350	£1650	*
1887 S	£185	£270	£900	£3250
1887 M	£185	£500	£1700	*
JH/shield				
1887	*	*	£190	£250
1887 proof	*	*	£750	£1850
1887 M	*	£185	£500	£2600
1887 S	*	£185	£500	£2500
1889 S	*	£200	£700	*
1890	*	*	£225	£325
1891	*	*	£250	£350
1891 S	£190	£325	£900	£3250
1892	*	*	£225	£300
1893	*	*	£225	£300
1893 M	*	£225	£625	£1500
OH/St George and dragon				
1893	*	*	£180	£285
1893 proof	*	*	£800	£2000
1893 M				ext. rare
1893 S	*	£195	£600	£1900
1894	*	*	£185	£285
1895	*	*	£185	£285
1896	*	*	£185	£285
1896 M	*	£185	£600	*
1897	*	*	£185	£285
1897 S	*	£185	£600	£1900
1898	*	*	£185	£240
1899	*	*	£145	£240
1899 M	£185	£225	£600	£1900
1899 P proof only	*	*	*	ext. rare
1900	*	*	£185	£285
1900 M	*	£185	£625	*
1900 P	£185	£270	£900	£2800
1900 S	*	£195	£376	£1400
1901	*	*	£185	£285
1901 P proof only	*	*	*	ext. rare
EDWARD VII				
1902	*	*	£185	£210
1902 proof	*	*	£225	£500
1902 S	*	*	£275	£800
1903	*	*	£185	£210
1903 S	*	*	£300	£1200
1904	*	*	£185	£210
1904 P	*	*	*	ext.rare
1905	*	*	£185	£210
1906	*	*	£185	£210
1906 M	£185	£350	£1400	*

	F	VF	EF	Unc
906 S	*	*	£200	£675
907	*	*	£185	£225
907 M	*	*	£325	£950
908	*	*	£185	£210
908 M	*	*	£285	£750
908 P	*	£485	£1400	*
908 S	*	*	£185	£675
909	*	*	£185	£210
909 M	*	*	£300	£900
909 P	*	£350	£825	*
910	*	*	£185	£210
910 S	*	*	£185	£600

GEORGE V

	F	VF	EF	Unc
911	*	*	*	£195
911 proof	*	*	£390	£950
911 P	*	*	£180	£290
911 S	*	*	£180	£290
912	*	*	*	£195
912 S	*	*	£180	£195
913	*	*	*	£195
914	*	*	*	£195
914 S	*	*	£180	£195
915	*	*	*	£195
915 M	*	*	£180	£195
915 P	*	*	£180	£270
915 S	*	*	£180	£195
916 S	*	*	£180	£195
918 P	*	£1300	£2900	£5200
923 SA proof	*	*	*	£1750
925 SA	*	*	*	£185
926 SA	*	*	*	£185

GEORGE VI

	F	VF	EF	Unc
937 proof	*	*	*	£1000

ELIZABETH II

	Unc
953 proof	ext. rare
980 proof	£185
982 proof	£200
982 BU	BV
983 proof	£240
984 proof	£240
985 proof	£240
986 proof	£240
987 proof	£240
988 proof	£285
989 500th anniversary of the sovereign, proof	£550
990 proof	£240
991 proof	£240
992 proof	£240
993 proof	£240
994 proof	£240
995 proof	£240
996 proof	£240
997 proof	£240
998 proof	£240
999 proof	£240
000 proof	£285

	Unc
2000 BU	BV
2001 proof	£235
2001 BU	£BV
2002 shield, proof	£300
2002 BU	BV
2003 proof	£235
2003 BU	BV
2004 proof	£245
2004 BU	BV
2005 proof	£235
2005 BU	BV
2006 proof	£235
2006 BU	BV
2007 proof	£235
2007 BU	BV
2008 BU	BV
2008 proof	£235
2009 BU	BV
2009 proof	£235
2010 BU	BV
2010 proof	£230
2011 BU	BV
2011 proof	£230
2012 BU	BV
2012 proof	£320
2013 BU	BV
2013 proof	£230
2014 BU	BV
2014 proof	£225
2014 BU "I" mint mark	BV
2015 proof	£225
2015 BU	BV
2015 proof, new portrait	£225
2016 BU	BV
2016 proof	£370
2017 BU	BV
2017 proof	£365
2018 BU	BV
2018 proof	£260
2019 proof	£365
2019 BU	BV

■ CROWNS

Exceptionally well struck coins of the early milled series can command considerably higher prices.

CROMWELL	F	VF	EF
1658	£2700	£4750	£9750
1658 Dutch copy	£4250	£5000	£14500
1658 Tanner's copy	*	£4750	£13000

CHARLES II	F	VF	EF
1662 1st bust	£250	£900	£9250
1663	£250	£900	£9250
1664 2nd bust	£250	£950	£10000
1665	£900	£2350	*
1666	£350	£1500	£12500
1666 eleph	£900	£3000	£14500

	F	VF	EF
1667	£250	£750	£7500
1668	£225	£675	£7500
1668/7	£225	£675	£7000
1668/5			ext. rare
1669	£375	£1400	*
1669/8	£400	£1500	
1670	£225	£675	£7000
1670/69	£450	£800	*
1671	£225	£675	£7000
1671 3rd bust	£225	£675	£7000
1672	£225	£675	£7000
1673	£225	£675	£7000
1673/2	£225	£675	£7000
1674	*	*	ext. rare
1675	£750	£2400	*
1675/3	£700	£1950	*
1676	£225	£650	£5500
1677	£225	£650	£5500
1677/6	£225	£650	£5500
1678/7	£300	£900	*
1679	£225	£650	£5500
1679 4th bust	£225	£650	£5500
1680 3rd bust	£300	£750	£6750
1680/79 3rd bust	£300	£750	£6750
1680 4th bust	£300	£750	£6750
1680/79	£325	£750	*
1681 eleph & castle	£4500	£9000	*
1681	£285	£725	£6700
1682	£265	£725	£6700
1682/1	£285	£725	£6700
1683	£350	£900	*
1684	£225	£800	*

JAMES II

	F	VF	EF
1686 1st bust	£450	£1600	*
1687 2nd bust	£225	£650	£2500
1688	£225	£650	£2700
1688/7	£225	£650	£2700

WILLIAM & MARY

	F	VF	EF
1691	£650	£1750	£5700
1692	£650	£1750	£5700
1692/2 inv QVINTO	£650	£1750	£5700
1692/2 inv QVARTO	£675	£1800	£6000

WILLIAM III

	F	VF	EF
1695 1st bust	£140	£350	£2200
1696	£160	£375	£2500
1696 GEI error	£700	£1500	*
1696/5	£250	£550	*
1696 2nd bust			unique
1696 3rd bust	£140	£350	£2200
1697	£1000	£4000	£18500
1700 3rd bust var	£140	£450	£2750

ANNE

	F	VF	EF
1703 1st bust VIGO	£450	£1250	£5000
1705	£700	£2000	£6000
1706	£325	£775	£3000

	F	VF	EF
1707	£300	£800	£3500
1707 2nd bust	£200	£500	£2250
1707 E	£200	£500	£2500
1708	£200	£500	£2200
1708 E	£200	£575	*
1708/7	£200	£575	*
1708 plumes	£325	£650	£3500
1713 3rd bust	£300	£800	£2750

GEORGE I

	F	VF	EF
1716 rev r & p	£425	£950	£4500

ABOVE: George I 1716 Crown

	F	VF	EF
1718	£425	£1250	£4750
1718/6	£475	£1400	£5200
1720	£475	£1400	£5200
1720/18	£425	£1250	£5200
1723 SS C	£425	£1250	£4750
1726 small r & p	£800	£1700	£7200

GEORGE II

	F	VF	EF
1732 YH	£420	£880	£3600
1732 proof	*	*	£19000
1734	£450	£900	£4000
1735	£450	£900	£4000
1736	£425	£875	£3250
1739	£325	£750	£2700
1741	£400	£725	£2700
1743 OH	£325	£725	£2700
1746 OH LIMA	£425	£825	£3000
1746 OH proof	*	£2500	£6000
1750	£425	£825	£3000
1751	£450	£850	£3500

ABOVE: William & Mary 1691 Crown

GEORGE III	F	VF	EF
Oval counterstamp	£300	£425	£900
Octagonal counterstamp	£575	£1000	£2000
1804 Bank of England Dollar	£200	£350	£800

Collectors should beware of contemporary forgeries on these three coins. The counterstamps are usually on Spanish–American dollars.

	F	VF	EF	Unc
1818 LVIII	£45	£85	£500	£1200
1818 LVIII error edge	£300	*	*	*
1818 LIX	£45	£85	£500	£1200
1819 LIX	£45	£85	£500	£1200
1819 LIX no edge stops	£80	£200	£600	*
1819/8 LIX	£75	£180	£600	*
1819 LIX no stop after TUTAMEN	£75	£180	£600	*
1820 LX	*	*	£500	£1200
1820/19 LX	£75	£225	£625	*

GEORGE IV

	F	VF	EF	Unc
1821 1st hd SECUNDO	£60	£175	£925	£2200

ABOVE: George IV 1821 Crown

	F	VF	EF	Unc
1821 SECUNDO proof	*	*	*	£5000
1821 TERTIO proof error edge	*	*	*	£6500
1822 SECUNDO	£75	£200	£950	£2500
1822 SECUNDO proof	*	*	*	*
1822 TERTIO	£75	£200	£950	£2500
1822 TERTIO proof	*	*	*	£6500
1823 proof only	*	*	*	ext. rare
1826 2nd head proof	*	*	£6750	£18500

WILLIAM IV proof only

	F	VF	EF	Unc
1831 W.W.	*	*	£11000	£28500
1831 W.WYON	*	*	£13000	£37000
1834 W.W.	*	*	£22000	£60000

VICTORIA	F	VF	EF	Unc
1839 proof	*	*	£9000	£29500
1844 star stops	£50	£125	£1100	£4250
1844 star stops proof	*	*	ext. rare	*
1844 cinquefoil stops	£50	£125	£1100	£4250
1845	£50	£125	£1100	£4250
1845 proof	*	*	*	£27500
1847	£70	£150	£1200	£5000

ABOVE: Victoria 1847 Gothic Crown

	F	VF	EF	Unc
1847 Gothic	£750	£1300	£3250	£10000
1847 Gothic plain edge	*	£1600	£3750	£15000
1853 SEPTIMO	*	*	£12500	£30000
1853 plain	*	*	£14000	£32500
1887 JH	£18	£30	£90	£175
1887 JH proof	*	*	£800	£3000
1888 close date	£30	£70	£170	£300
1888 wide date	£80	£200	£500	*
1889	£30	£70	£150	£300
1890	£30	£70	£150	£300
1891	£30	£70	£175	£375
1892	£30	£85	£200	£425
1893 LVI	£30	£70	£185	£375
1893 LVI proof	*	*	£1000	£3250
1893 LVII	£30	£80	£300	£600
1894 LVII	£30	£80	£275	£500
1894 LVIII	£30	£80	£275	£500
1895 LVIII	£30	£80	£275	£450
1895 LIX	£30	£90	£325	£650
1896 LIX	£45	£90	£325	£650
1896 LX	£30	£80	£275	£475
1897 LX	£30	£80	£240	£450
1897 LXI	£30	£45	£185	£385
1898 LXI	£25	£80	£240	£450
1898 LXII	£30	£90	£350	£700
1899 LXII	£30	£80	£240	£475
1899 LXIII	£30	£80	£240	£475
1900 LXIII	£30	£80	£260	£550
1900 LXIV	£30	£80	£225	£425

EDWARD VII

	F	VF	EF	Unc
1902	£45	£100	£225	£400

	F	VF	EF	Unc
1902 matt proof	*	*	£250	£450
GEORGE V				
1927 proof	*	*	£200	£375
1928	£100	£185	£310	£475
1929	£100	£185	£310	£475
1930	£100	£170	£300	£425
1931	£100	£170	£300	£425
1932	£170	£270	£450	£750
1933	£100	£170	£300	£425
1934	£1000	£2000	£3250	£5000
1935	£20	£25	£30	£35
1935 raised edge proof	*	*	*	£750
1935 gold proof	*	*	*	£55000
1935 proof in good silver (.925)	*	*	*	£3000
1935 specimen	*	*	*	£100
1936	£175	£275	£450	£800

ABOVE: George V 1935 raised edge proof Crown

GEORGE VI				
1937	*	*	£25	£35
1937 proof	*	*	*	£85
1937 'VIP' proof	*	*	*	ext. rare
1951	*	*	*	£10
1951 'VIP' proof	*	*	*	£950

ELIZABETH II				
1953	*	*	*	£8
1953 proof	*	*	*	£37
1953 'VIP' proof	*	*	*	£800
1960	*	*	*	£10
1960 'VIP' proof	*	*	*	£850
1960 polished dies	*	*	*	£30
1965 Churchill	*	*	*	£5
1965 Churchill 'satin' finish	*	*	*	£2000

For issues from 1972 onwards see under 25 pence in Decimal Coinage section.

◾ DOUBLE–FLORINS

VICTORIA	F	VF	EF	Unc
1887 Roman 'I'	£20	£30	£75	£150
1887 Roman 'I' proof	*	*	£350	£1350
1887 Arabic '1'	£20	£30	£75	£150
1887 Arabic '1' proof	*	*	£350	£1350
1888	£20	£30	£85	£200
1888 inv '1'	£30	£50	£200	£475
1889	£20	£30	£85	£200
1889 inv '1'	£30	£50	£200	£475
1890	£20	£30	£85	£200

◾ THREE SHILLING BANK TOKENS

Contemporary forgeries of these pieces, as well as of other George III coins, were produced in quite large numbers. Several varieties exist for the pieces dated 1811 and 1812. Prices given here are for the commonest types of these years.

GEORGE III				
1811	£20	£60	£175	£325
1812 draped bust	£20	£60	£175	£325
1812 laureate hd	£20	£60	£175	£325
1813	£20	£60	£165	£325
1814	£20	£60	£175	£325
1815	£20	£60	£165	£325
1816	*	£325	£1000	£1800

◾ HALFCROWNS

CROMWELL	F	VF	EF
1656	£3000	£7250	£16000
1658	£1500	£2800	£6000

ABOVE: Cromwell 1658 Halfcrown

CHARLES II			
1663 1st bust	£300	£1000	£8000
1664 2nd bust	£325	£1400	£8000
1666/3 3rd bust	£900	*	*
1666/3 eleph	£120	£3000	*

	F	VF	EF
1667/4			ext. rare
1668/4	£300	£1200	*
1669	£400	£1000	*
1669/4	£300	£1000	*
1670	£175	£600	£3900
1671 3rd bust var	£175	£600	£3900
1671/0	£175	£600	£3900
1672	£175	£600	£3900
1672 4th bust	£175	£600	£3750
1673	£150	£575	£3900
1673 plume below	£9000	*	*
1673 plume both sides	£9000	*	*
1674	£175	£600	£3900
1674/3	£300	£800	*
1675	£150	£500	£3000
1676	£150	£500	£3000
1677	£150	£500	£3000
1678	£200	£700	*
1679	£175	£550	£3000
1680	£200	£600	£3900
1681	£175	£550	£3900
1681/0	£300	£800	*
1681 eleph & castle	£3000	£7750	£26000
1682	£175	£550	£3900
1682/79	£350	£900	*
1683	£175	£600	£3900
1683 plume below	ext. rare	*	*
1684/3	£350	£900	

JAMES II

	F	VF	EF
1685 1st bust	£225	£900	£4000
1686	£225	£900	£4000
1686/5	£300	£950	*
1687	£225	£900	£4000
1687/6	£550	£900	£3750
1687 2nd bust	£225	£850	£3750
1688	£240	£900	£4000

WILLIAM AND MARY

	F	VF	EF
1689 1st busts 1st shield	£125	£425	£2000
1689 1st busts 2nd shield	£125	£425	£2000

ABOVE: William and Mary 1690 Halfcrown

	F	VF	EF
1690	£175	£600	£3250
1691 2nd busts 3rd shield	£130	£450	£3000
1692	£130	£450	£3000
1693	£130	£450	£3000
1693 2nd busts 3rd shield 3 inv	£150	£500	£3250
1693 3 over 3 inv	£130	£450	£3000

WILLIAM III

	F	VF	EF
1696 1st bust large shield early hp	£70	£275	£980
1696 B	£120	£325	£2600
1696 C	£175	£475	£3200
1696 E	£175	£450	£2700
1696 N	£225	£750	*
1696 Y	£130	£400	£2700
1696 y/E			ext. rare
1696 large shield ord hp	£175	£400	£1400
1696 C	£175	£450	£2700
1696 E	£175	£450	£2700
1696 N	£275	£700	*
1696 small shield	£85	£285	£2350
1696 B	£185	£525	£2350
1696 C	£185	£525	£2350
1696 E	£185	£525	£2350
1696 N	£170	£450	£2300
1696 y	£170	£450	£2300
1696 2nd bust			unique
1697 1st bust large shield	£80	£250	£925
1697 B	£125	£325	£2300
1697 C	£125	£325	£2250
1697 E	£110	£295	£2300
1697 E/C	£170	£550	*
1697 N	£125	£325	£2300
1697 y	£125	£325	£2300
1698	£80	£220	£825
1699	£160	£400	£2300
1700	£75	£180	£800
1701	£100	£350	£1400
1701 eleph & castle	£3000	*	*
1701 plumes	£300	£1000	£5500

ANNE

	F	VF	EF
1703 plain	£800	£2000	£9500
1703 VIGO	£200	£475	£1850
1704 plumes	£275	£800	£3500
1705	£200	£600	£2500
1706 r & p	£140	£325	£1500
1707	£125	£280	£1400
1707 plain	£90	£225	£1000
1707 E	£95	£250	£1450
1708 plain	£90	£325	£900
1708 E	£95	£325	£2300
1708 plumes	£175	£425	£1800
1709 plain	£90	£260	£925
1709 E	£500	*	*
1710 r & p	£140	£375	£1500
1712	£100	£250	£1500
1713 plain	£100	£325	£1500
1713 r & p	£100	£300	£1300
1714	£90	£285	£1275

MILLED COINAGE

	F	VF	EF
1714/3	£150	£475	£1500

GEORGE I

	F	VF	EF
1715 proof	*	*	£7000
1715 r & p	£250	£600	£3000
1717	£250	£600	£3500
1720	£250	£600	£3000
1720/17	£250	£600	£3000
1723 SS C	£225	£550	£2700
1726 small r & p	£2750	£4700	£14000

GEORGE II

	F	VF	EF
1731 YH proof	*	£2750	£8000
1731	£170	£475	£1850
1732	£170	£475	£1850
1734	£190	£550	£2000
1735	£175	£475	£1850
1736	£190	£550	£2000
1739	£140	£300	£1600
1741	£160	£310	£1650
1741/39	£140	£310	£1600
1743 OH	£100	£250	£1000
1745	£100	£250	£1000
1745 LIMA	£85	£185	£750
1746 LIMA	£75	£185	£750
1746 plain, proof	*	*	£5000
1750	£180	£425	£2100
1751	£185	£485	£2200

GEORGE III

	F	VF	EF	Unc
Oval counterstamp, usually				
on Spanish Half-Dollar	£275	£425	£800	*
1816 large hd	£15	£55	£300	£650
1817	£15	£55	£300	£650
1817 small hd	£15	£55	£300	£650

ABOVE: George III oval countermarked
Spanish 4 Reales (Half-Dollar)

	F	VF	EF	Unc
1818	£15	£55	£350	£700
1819	£15	£55	£300	£650
1819/8				ext. rare
1820	£15	£55	£300	£650

GEORGE IV
1st hd

	F	VF	EF	Unc
1820 1st rev	£30	£80	£350	£750

	F	VF	EF	Unc
1821	£35	£85	£375	£800
1821 proof	*	*	£1200	£3000
1823	£1200	£2800	£9750	*
1823 2nd rev	£35	£95	£425	£900
1824	£40	£100	£450	£1000

ABOVE: George IV 1820 Halfcrown

2nd hd

	F	VF	EF	Unc
1824 3rd rev				ext. rare
1825	£35	£75	£385	£750
1826	£35	£75	£385	£825
1826 proof	*	*	£1200	£3500
1828	£70	£175	£800	£2300
1829	£45	£100	£400	£1000

WILLIAM IV

	F	VF	EF	Unc
1831				ext. rare
1831 proof	*	*	£1000	£3750
1834 ww	£40	£150	£550	£1350
1834 ww in script	£30	£85	£385	£925
1835	£40	£125	£485	£1250
1836	£30	£80	£375	£850
1836/5	£50	£170	£650	*
1837	£50	£150	£625	£1400

ABOVE: William IV 1831 proof Halfcrown

VICTORIA

From time to time Halfcrowns bearing dates ranging from 1861 to 1871 are found (usually worn), but except for rare proofs in 1853, 1862 and 1864, no Halfcrowns were struck between 1850 and 1874, so pieces dated from this period are now considered to be contemporary or later forgeries.

ABOVE: Victoria 1839 proof Halfcrown

Young Head	F	VF	EF	Unc
1839 ww in relief	£900	£1800	£7000	*
1839 plain and ornate fillets, plain edge proof	*	*	£2000	£6000
1839 ww incuse	£1000	£2600	£8000	*
1840	£50	£130	£650	£1750
1841	£600	£1400	£4900	*
1842	£50	£120	£700	£1800
1843	£100	£275	£2200	£4000
1844	£50	£120	£700	£1800
1845	£50	£120	£700	£1800
1846	£50	£120	£700	£1800
1848	£200	£575	£1800	£4000
1848/6	£175	£500	£1650	£3500
1849 large date	£75	£200	£800	£2000
1849 small date	£100	£325	£1000	£2500
1850	£70	£220	£800	£2100
1853 proof	*	*	*	£8000
1862 proof	*	*	*	£9500
1864 proof	*	*	*	£9500
1874	£20	£60	£250	£680
1875	£20	£60	£250	£680
1876	£20	£60	£250	£680
1876/5	£25	£70	£400	£825
1877	£20	£60	£250	£680
1878	£20	£60	£250	£680
1879	£20	£60	£320	£825
1880	£20	£60	£250	£575
1881	£20	£60	£250	£575
1882	£20	£60	£325	£800
1883	£20	£60	£250	£575
1884	£20	£60	£250	£575

	F	VF	EF	Unc
1885	£20	£60	£250	£575
1886	£20	£60	£250	£575
1887	£20	£60	£250	£575
Jubilee Head				
1887	£10	£18	£40	£90
1887 proof	*	*	£275	£800
1888	£10	£25	£75	£200
1889	£10	£25	£75	£200
1890	£10	£30	£80	£220
1891	£10	£30	£90	£285
1892	£10	£30	£90	£260
Old Head				
1893	£10	£25	£65	£140
1893 proof	*	*	£295	£950
1894	£12	£30	£120	£275

ABOVE: Edward VII 1909 Halfcrown

	F	VF	EF	Unc
1895	£10	£30	£95	£210
1896	£10	£30	£95	£210
1897	£10	£28	£70	£200
1898	£10	£30	£90	£180
1899	£10	£28	£75	£195
1900	£10	£22	£55	£150
1901	£10	£28	£70	£160
EDWARD VII				
1902	£15	£35	£90	£180
1902 matt proof	*	*	*	£275
1903	£150	£425	£2200	£5000
1904	£60	£250	£900	£2200
1905 F	£650	£1400	£6000	£12500
1906	£18	£50	£240	£675
1907	£18	£50	£240	£675
1908	£25	£70	£450	£1500
1909	£18	£60	£375	£900
1910	£18	£50	£185	£450
GEORGE V				
1911	*	£12	£605	£210

	F	VF	EF	Unc
1911 proof	*	*	*	£350
1912	*	£18	£70	£325
1913	*	£18	£80	£340
1914	*	*	£28	£100
1915	*	*	£25	£85
1916	*	*	£25	£80
1917	*	*	£32	£90
1918	*	*	£22	£70
1919	*	*	£28	£100
1920	*	*	£35	£180
1921	*	*	£45	£180
1922	*	*	£35	£120
1923	*	*	£15	£50
1924	*	*	£35	£110
1925	*	£55	£375	£900
1926	*	*	£50	£170
1926 mod eff	*	*	£70	£200
1927	*	*	£25	£65
1927 new rev, proof only	*	*	*	£120
1928	*	*	£15	£30
1929	*	*	£15	£30
1930	£9	£40	£300	£1000
1931	*	*	£15	£50
1932	*	*	£20	£60
1933	*	*	£12	£40
1934	*	*	£45	£150
1935	*	*	£10	£30
1936	*	*	£10	£25

GEORGE VI

	F	VF	EF	Unc
1937	*	*	*	£18
1937 proof	*	*	*	£35
1938	*	*	£10	£40
1939	*	*	*	£20
1940	*	*	*	£16
1941	*	*	*	£16
1942	*	*	*	£14
1943	*	*	*	£14
1944	*	*	*	£14
1945	*	*	*	£14
1946	*	*	*	£12
1947	*	*	*	£10
1948	*	*	*	£10
1949	*	*	*	£17
1950	*	*	*	£25
1950 proof	*	*	*	£28
1951	*	*	*	£26
1951 proof	*	*	*	£28
1952				2 known

ELIZABETH II

	F	VF	EF	Unc
1953	*	*	*	£12
1953 proof	*	*	*	£18
1954	*	*	£6	£50
1955	*	*	*	£11
1956	*	*	*	£11
1957	*	*	*	£9
1958	*	*	*	£30
1959	*	*	*	£50

	F	VF	EF	Unc
1960	*	*	*	£5
1961	*	*	*	£5
1962	*	*	*	£5
1963	*	*	*	£3
1964	*	*	*	£3
1965	*	*	*	£3
1966	*	*	*	£2
1967	*	*	*	£2

■ FLORINS

The first Florins produced in the reign of Victoria bore the legend VICTORIA REGINA and the date, omitting DEI GRATIA or 'By the Grace of God'. They are therefore known as 'godless' Florins.

The date of a Victorian Gothic Florin is shown in Roman numerals in Gothic lettering on the obverse, for example mdccclvii (1857). Gothic Florins were issued between 1851–1887.

VICTORIA

	F	VF	EF	Unc
1848 'Godless' proof with milled edge	*	*	*	£4500
1848 'Godless' proof with plain edge	*	*	*	£3500
1849 'Godless' ww obliterated by circle	£30	£70	£250	£550
1849 'Godless' ww inside circle	£25	£55	£200	£450
1851 proof only	*	*	*	£16000
1852	£22	£50	£170	£500
1853	£22	£50	£170	£500
1853 no stop after date	£22	£55	£210	£550
1853 proof	*	*	*	£5000
1854	£700	£1750	£6000	*
1855	£22	£60	£270	£700
1856	£22	£60	£270	£700
1857	£22	£50	£260	£700
1858	£22	£50	£260	£700
1859	£22	£50	£260	£700
1859 no stops after date	£22	£50	£250	£690
1860	£22	£55	£270	£780
1862	£200	£450	£1750	£4500
1863	£700	£1800	£5500	*
1864	£22	£55	£250	£700
1865	£40	£110	£420	£825

ABOVE: Victoria 1871 Gothic Florin

	F	VF	EF	Unc
1865 colon after date	*	*	£950	*
1866	£35	£85	£270	£655
1866 colon after date				ext. rare
1867	£35	£80	£240	£700
1868	£35	£90	£325	£750
1869	£35	£90	£300	£725
1870	£22	£55	£250	£700
1871	£22	£55	£250	£700
1872	£22	£40	£240	£660
1873	£22	£40	£210	£620
1874	£22	£45	£240	£660
1874 xxiv/iii die	£80	£220	£525	*
1875	£22	£50	£240	£640
1876	£22	£50	£220	£610
1877	£22	£50	£230	£635
1877 no ww	*	*	*	ext. rare
1877 42 arcs	£35	£90	£340	£700
1878	£22	£50	£210	£560
1879 die no	*	*	*	ext.rare
1879 ww 42 arcs	£95	£210	£600	*
1879 ww 48 arcs	£22	£45	£210	£635
1879 no ww, 38 arcs	£22	£45	£210	£550
1880	£22	£45	£200	£485
1881	£22	£45	£200	£485
1881 xxri error	£30	£90	£325	£550
1883	£22	£45	£200	£460
1884	£22	£45	£200	£460
1885	£22	£45	£200	£460
1886	£22	£45	£195	£420
1887 46 arcs	£35	£80	£260	£650
1887 JH	*	£13	£30	£70
1887 JH proof	*	*	*	£500
1888	*	£18	£60	£140
1889	*	£22	£90	£190
1890	*	£30	£175	£440
1891	£25	£65	£280	£550
1892	£25	£70	£310	£625
1893 OH	*	£18	£55	£130
1893 proof	*	*	*	£625
1894	*	£25	£100	£270
1895	*	£20	£75	£220
1896	*	£20	£75	£220
1897	*	£20	£70	£175
1898	*	£20	£75	£220
1899	*	£20	£75	£220
1900	*	£20	£65	£130
1901	*	£20	£65	£130

EDWARD VII

	F	VF	EF	Unc
1902	*	£15	£60	£115
1902 matt proof	*	*	*	£120
1903	*	£30	£160	£425
1904	*	£50	£200	£550
1905	£70	£185	£850	£1850
1906	*	£30	£140	£425
1907	*	£35	£150	£450
1908	*	£50	£290	£575
1909	*	£45	£290	£580
1910	*	£22	£130	£300

ABOVE: George V 1932 Florin

	F	VF	EF	Unc
GEORGE V				
1911	*	*	*	£130
1911 proof	*	*	*	£220
1912	*	*	£55	£170
1913	*	*	£75	£240
1914	*	*	£28	£80
1915	*	*	£50	£110
1916	*	*	£30	£80
1917	*	*	£40	£85
1918	*	*	£40	£85
1919	*	*	£32	£80
1920	*	*	£40	£140
1921	*	*	£32	£110
1922	*	*	£22	£90
1923	*	*	£20	£55
1924	*	*	£30	£60
1925	*	£40	£175	£550
1926	*	*	£50	£100
1927 proof	*	*	*	£130
1928	*	*	£10	£28
1929	*	*	£10	£35
1930	*	*	£30	£75
1931	*	*	£15	£55
1932	£20	£65	£325	£950
1933	*	*	£14	£50
1935	*	*	£10	£30
1936	*	*	£7	£22
GEORGE VI				
1937	*	*	*	£13
1937 proof	*	*	*	£25
1938	*	*	*	£40
1939	*	*	*	£14
1940	*	*	*	£18
1941	*	*	*	£12
1942	*	*	*	£9
1943	*	*	*	£12
1944	*	*	*	£12
1945	*	*	*	£9
1946	*	*	*	£9
1947	*	*	*	£9
1948	*	*	*	£9
1949	*	*	*	£22
1950	*	*	*	£22
1950 proof	*	*	*	£24
1951	*	*	*	£27
1951 proof	*	*	*	£28

ELIZABETH II	F	VF	EF	Unc
1953	*	*	*	£9
1953 proof	*	*	*	£15
1954	*	*	*	£50
1955	*	*	*	£7
1956	*	*	*	£7
1957	*	*	*	£50
1958	*	*	*	£35
1959	*	*	*	£40
1960	*	*	*	£4
1961	*	*	*	£4
1962	*	*	*	£2
1963	*	*	*	£2
1964	*	*	*	£2
1965	*	*	*	£2
1966	*	*	*	£1
1967	*	*	*	£1

■ EIGHTEENPENCE BANK TOKENS

GEORGE III				
1811	£15	£30	£120	£240
1812	£15	£30	£120	£240
1812 laureate hd	£15	£30	£120	£240
1813	£15	£30	£120	£240
1814	£15	£30	£120	£240
1815	£15	£30	£120	£240
1816	£15	£30	£120	£240

■ SHILLINGS

ABOVE: Cromwell 1658 Shilling

CROMWELL	F	VF	EF
1658	£1000	£1850	£3750
1658 Dutch copy	*	*	£12000

ABOVE: Charles II 1671 Shilling, plumes both sides

CHARLES II	F	VF	EF
1663 1st bust	£150	£550	£3000
1663 1st bust var	£150	£400	£3000
1666 1st bust	*	*	*
1666 eleph	£700	£2800	£9200
1666 guinea head, eleph	£2850	*	*
1666 2nd bust	£1750	*	*
1668 1st bust var	£420	£1700	*
1668 2nd bust	£150	£550	£2600
1668/7	£170	£620	£2700
1669/6 1st bust var	ext. rare	*	*
1669 2nd bust	ext. rare	*	*
1670	£170	£625	£2350
1671	£170	£650	£2600
1671 plumes both sides	£800	£2000	£5750
1672	£170	£625	£2600
1673	£170	£625	£2600
1673/2	£170	£625	£2600
1673 plumes both sides	£800	£2000	£5750
1674	£170	£550	£2600
1674/3	£170	£625	£2600
1674 plumes both sides	£800	£2300	£5250
1674 plumes rev only	£1250	£3600	*
1674 3rd bust	£550	£1600	*
1675	£550	£1600	*
1675/3	£550	£1600	£4000
1675/4 2nd bust	£350	£1150	*
1675 plumes both sides	£925	£2600	*
1676	£175	£700	£2350
1676/5	£175	£700	£2350
1676 plumes both sides	£950	£2600	£5600
1677	£170	£550	£2600
1677 plumes obv only	£950	£2300	£5300
1678	£175	£700	*
1678/7	£180	£725	*
1679	£170	£625	£2600
1679/7	£170	£625	£2600
1679 plumes	£925	£2600	£5600
1679 plumes obv only	£1600	£3300	*
1680/79 plumes	£1500	*	*
1681	£650	£1600	*
1681/0	£700	£1700	*
1681/0 eleph & castle	£3100	£8800	*
1682/1	£1000	*	*
1683	£1000	*	*
1683 4th bust	£300	£775	£2900
1684	£300	£775	£2900
1685	£250	£600	£2400

ABOVE: James II 1687 Shilling

JAMES II	F	VF	EF
1685 no stops on rev	£240	£600	£2750
1685 plume on rev			ext. rare
1686	£240	£600	£2500
1686/5	£240	£600	£2500
1686 V/S	£240	£600	£2500
1687	£240	£600	£2500
1687/6	£240	£600	£2350
1688	£225	£575	£2500
1688/7	£240	£600	£2500

WILLIAM AND MARY			
1692	£270	£675	£2700
1693	£270	£675	£2700

WILLIAM III			
1695 1st bust	£40	£130	£550
1696	£35	£120	£475
1696 no stops on rev	£170	£360	£775
1669 in error	£900	*	*
1696 B	£50	£175	£875
1696 C	£75	£210	£980
1696 E	£65	£200	£875
1696 N	£89	£275	*
1696 y	£65	£200	£775
1696 Y	£95	£320	*
1696 2nd bust		unique	
1696 3rd bust C	£170	£580	*
1696 E		ext. rare	
1696 y		ext. rare	
1697 1st bust	£40	£110	£480
1697 no stops on rev	£90	£300	£750
1697 B	£95	£290	£730
1697 C	£110	£370	£750

ABOVE: William III 1699 roses Shilling

	F	VF	EF
1697 E	£95	£290	£730
1697 N	£130	£330	*
1697 y	£95	£290	£730
1697 Y	£95	£300	£880
1697 3rd bust	£35	£110	£460
1697 B	£130	£370	£1300
1697 C	£80	£260	£825
1697 E	£95	£320	£1000
1697 N	£110	£350	£1375
1697 y	£95	£340	£1150
1697 3rd bust var	£40	£120	£500
1697 B	£120	£390	£1400
1697 C	£170	£420	£1625

	F	VF	EF
1698 plain	£80	£270	£930
1698 plumes	£260	£770	£3000
1698 4th bust	£310	£770	£3000
1699 4th bust	£310	£750	£2750
1699 5th bust	£190	£475	£2000
1699 plumes	£270	£575	£3200
1699 roses	£350	£775	*
1700	£35	£110	£500
1700 no stops on rev	£85	£275	£825
1700 plume below bust	£3000	*	*
1701	£90	£300	£1150
1701 plumes	£275	£600	£3000

	F	VF	EF
1711 3rd bust	£180	£500	£1250
1711 4th bust	£40	£100	£400
1712 r&p	£60	£180	£600
1713/2	£70	£220	£700
1714	£70	£180	£600
1714/3	£70	£275	£725

ABOVE: George I 1721/0 roses & plumes Shilling

ABOVE: Anne 1702 Shilling

ANNE

	F	VF	EF
1702 1st bust	£95	£270	£1125
1702 plumes	£100	£320	£950
1702 VIGO	£100	£300	£950
1703 2nd bust VIGO	£100	£300	£950
1704	£550	£1600	£3800
1704 plumes	£220	£490	£1900
1705	£200	£500	£1950
1705 plumes	£150	£425	£1800
1705 r&p	£125	£350	£1200
1707 r&p	£130	£390	£1375
1707 E	£80	£270	£925
1707 E*	£110	£320	£1400
1707 E* local dies	£240	£725	*
1707 3rd bust	£30	£150	£475
1707 plumes	£90	£300	£1125
1707 E	£70	£240	£850
1707 Edin bust E*	£525	*	*
1708 2nd bust E	£180	£535	*
1708 E*	£270	£725	*
1708/7 E*		ext. rare	
1708 r&p	£160	£450	£1300
1708 3rd bust	£35	£110	£475
1708 plumes	£110	£325	£1150
1708 r&p	£135	£375	£1250
1708 E	£80	£240	£900
1708/7 E	£170	£325	£1125
1708 Edin bust E*	£270	£725	*
1709	£65	£110	£490
1709 Edin bust E	£380	£1125	*
1709 Edin bust E*	£110	£370	£1150
1710 3rd bust r&p	£90	£325	£950
1710 4th bust proof		ext. rare	
1710 r&p	£70	£220	£800

GEORGE I

	F	VF	EF
1715 1st bust r&p	£70	£200	£775
1716 r&p	£160	£390	£1250
1717 r&p	£90	£285	£825
1718 r&p	£65	£190	£775
1719 r&p	£160	£400	£1300
1720 r&p	£90	£300	£900
1720/18	£160	£500	£1500
1720 plain	£70	£180	£570
1720 large 0	£70	£190	£600
1721 plain	£185	£650	£1400
1721 r&p	£95	£300	£950
1721/0 r&p	£90	£275	£850
1721/19 r&p	£90	£275	£880
1721/18 r&p	ext. rare	*	*
1722 r&p	£90	£325	£900
1723 r&p	£90	£325	£900
1723 SSC	£35	£90	£325
1723 SSC C/SS	£40	£120	£400
1723 SSC French arms at date	£180	£550	£1600
1723 2nd bust SS C	£60	£135	£425
1723 r&p	£100	£320	£1000
1723 WCC	£750	£2000	£7000
1724 r&p	£100	£320	£1000
1724 WCC	£750	£2000	£7000
1725 r&p	£120	£350	£975
1725 no obv stops	£120	£350	£1100
1725 WCC	£750	£2000	£7000
1726 r&p	£650	£1800	*
1726 WCC	£750	£2000	£7000
1727 r&p	£525	£1300	£2900
1727 r&p no stops on obv	£525	£1300	£3000

GEORGE II

	F	VF	EF
1727 YH plumes	£180	£450	£1550
1727 r&p	£120	£320	£1825
1728	£160	£450	£1825
1728 r&p	£110	£300	£1375
1729 r&p	£100	£300	£1375
1731 r&p	£100	£300	£1500

	F	VF	EF
1731 plumes	£150	£450	£1700
1732 r&p	£90	£260	£980
1734 r&p	£90	£275	£980
1735 r&p	£90	£260	£980
1736 r&p	£85	£200	£850
1736/5 r&p	£90	£270	£950
1737 r&p	£90	£270	£950
1739 r&p roses	£60	£175	£650
1741 roses	£60	£175	£650
1741/39 roses	£110	£320	£1150

ABOVE: George II 1729 young head Shilling

1743 OH roses	£60	£150	£580
1743/1 roses	£70	£180	£680
1745	£50	£120	£490
1745/3 roses	£70	£180	£680
1745 LIMA	£35	£100	£450
1746 LIMA	£90	£220	£700
1746/5 LIMA	£90	£220	£750
1746 proof	*	£850	£2750
1747 roses	£60	£130	£575
1750	£60	£170	£625
1750/6	£80	£190	£680
1751	£90	£240	£875
1758	£20	£50	£175

ABOVE: George III 1763 'Northumberland' Shilling

GEORGE III

	F	VF	EF	Unc
1763 'Northumberland' F	*	£500	£1000	£1950
1764 pattern	*	*	*	£8000
1778 pattern	*	*	*	£9000
1786 proof or pattern	*	*	*	£9500
1787 no hearts	£20	£40	£80	£180
1787 no hearts no stop over head	£30	£60	£120	£250
1787 no hearts no stops at date	£25	£70	£160	£300

	F	VF	EF	Unc
1787 no stops on obv	£275	£625	*	*
1787 hearts	£25	£40	£80	£180
1798 'Dorrien and Magens'	£5500	£13000	£25000	*
1816	*	£12	£90	£175
1817	*	£12	£90	£175
1817 GEOE error	£80	£160	£500	*
1818	£12	£30	£150	£270
1819	*	£12	£95	£195
1819/8	*	*	£170	£340
1820	*	£12	£95	£195

GEORGE IV

	F	VF	EF	Unc
1820 1st head 1st rev pattern or proof	*	*	*	£5500
1821 1st rev	£15	£50	£195	£500
1821 proof	*	*	£800	£1950
1823 1st head 2nd rev	£35	£90	£350	£675
1824 2nd rev	£15	£45	£190	£475
1825 2nd rev	£20	£55	£220	£500
1825 2nd head	£15	£30	£160	£350
1826	*	£30	£130	£300

ABOVE: George IV 1824 Shilling

1826 proof	*	*	£335	£1000
1827	£30	£85	£370	£700
1829	*	£45	£220	£550

WILLIAM IV

1831 proof	*	*	£675	£1800
1834	£15	£40	£200	£500
1835	£15	£45	£220	£600
1836	£15	£40	£200	£500
1837	£30	£80	£270	£675

ABOVE: William IV 1836 Shilling

VICTORIA

1838 YH	£25	£30	£185	£475
1839	£28	£55	£260	£600

	F	VF	EF	Unc
1839 2nd YH	£15	£35	£175	£475
1839 proof	*	*	*	£1750
1840	£22	£50	£220	£500
1841	£22	£55	£290	£550
1842	£17	£35	£160	£475
1843	£30	£50	£220	£550
1844	£22	£35	£160	£475
1845	£22	£35	£150	£465
1846	£12	£35	£150	£465
1848/6	£80	£260	£725	*
1849	£18	£40	£180	£575
1850	£550	£1850	£4750	*
1850/49	£650	£1950	£4950	*
1851	£45	£160	£500	£1000
1852	£15	£25	£130	£475
1853	£15	£25	£130	£475
1853 proof	*	*	*	£3000
1854	£200	£450	£1800	£4750
1855	£15	£25	£150	£400
1856	£15	£25	£135	£350
1857	£15	£25	£135	£350
1857 F:G:	£260	£600	£2250	*
1858	£15	£25	£135	£350
1859	£15	£25	£135	£350
1860	£15	£40	£165	£600
1861	£15	£30	£160	£350
1862	£25	£55	£240	£550

	F	VF	EF	Unc
1878	£15	£30	£165	£400
1879 no die	ext. rare			
1879 4th YH	£12	£25	£130	£290
1880	£12	£20	£120	£240
1880 longer line below SHILLING	*	*	*	*
1881	£12	£25	£100	£220
1881 longer linebelow SHILLING	£12	£25	£100	£220
1881 longer line below SHILLING, large rev lettering	£12	£25	£100	£220
1882	£20	£30	£100	£320
1883	£12	£25	£100	£230
1884	£12	£25	£100	£230
1885	£12	£25	£100	£230
1886	£12	£25	£100	£230
1887	£15	£30	£125	£300
1887 JH	*	£8	£18	£40
1887 proof	*	*	*	£425
1888/7	*	£10	£50	£100
1889	£45	£110	£450	£700
1889 large JH	*	£10	£60	£165
1890	*	£10	£60	£165
1891	*	£10	£60	£165
1892	*	£10	£60	£165
1893 OH	£5	£15	£40	£100
1893 proof	*	*	*	£425
1893 small obv letters	*	*	£45	£100
1894	*	£15	£65	£130
1895	*	*	£45	£130
1896	*	*	£45	£130

ABOVE: Victoria 1860 Shilling

	F	VF	EF	Unc
1863	£45	£110	£525	£1200
1863/1	£65	£210	£700	*
1864	£15	£30	£135	£350
1865	£15	£30	£135	£350
1866	£15	£30	£135	£350
1866 BBRITANNIAR error	£100	£350	£900	£1850
1867	£15	£30	£135	£375
1867 3rd YH, die no	£200	£3575	£2000	£3000
1868	£12	£30	£130	£350
1869	£20	£45	£160	£375
1870	£12	£30	£150	£350
1871	£12	£25	£150	£350
1872	£12	£25	£140	£350
1873	£12	£25	£130	£350
1874	£12	£25	£130	£350
1875	£12	£25	£130	£350
1876	£12	£25	£130	£350
1877	£12	£25	£130	£350

ABOVE: Victoria 1896 Shilling

	F	VF	EF	Unc
1897	*	£10	£50	£130
1898	*	£10	£50	£130
1899	*	£10	£55	£140
1900	*	£10	£50	£130
1901	*	£10	£50	£130

EDWARD VII

	F	VF	EF	Unc
1902	*	*	£50	£90
1902 matt proof	*	*	£60	£125
1903	*	£30	£175	£450
1904	*	£20	£145	£395
1905	£95	£275	£1450	£3100
1906	*	*	£70	£190
1907	*	*	£75	£220

	F	VF	EF	Unc
1908	£10	£22	£190	£550
1909	£10	£22	£190	£550
1910	*	*	£50	£135

GEORGE V

	F	VF	EF	Unc
1911	*	*	£30	£80
1911 proof	*	*	*	£175
1912	*	*	£38	£140
1913	*	*	£80	£220
1914	*	*	£32	£70
1915	*	*	£32	£70
1916	*	*	£32	£70
1917	*	*	£45	£90
1918	*	*	£32	£70
1919	*	*	£45	£95
1920	*	*	£40	£85
1921	*	*	£50	£130
1922	*	*	£35	£85
1923	*	*	£28	£70
1923 nickel	*	*	*	£2000
1924	*	*	£32	£85
1924 nickel	*	*	*	£2000
1925	*	*	£65	£150
1926	*	*	£32	£75
1926 mod eff	*	*	£22	£55
1927	*	*	£30	£60
1927 new type	*	*	£15	£45
1927 new type proof	*	*	*	£75
1928	*	*	*	£27
1929	*	*	£9	£27
1930	*	*	£40	£120
1931	*	*	£9	£32
1932	*	*	£9	£32
1933	*	*	£9	£32
1934	*	*	£17	£55
1935	*	*	£5	£22
1936	*	*	£5	£22

GEORGE VI

	F	VF	EF	Unc
1937 Eng	*	*	*	£12
1937 Eng proof	*	*	*	£25
1937 Scot	*	*	*	£12
1937 Scot proof	*	*	*	£25
1938 Eng	*	*	£6	£37
1938 Scot	*	*	£6	£33
1939 Eng	*	*	*	£17
1939 Scot	*	*	*	£20
1940 Eng	*	*	*	£17
1940 Scot	*	*	*	£20
1941 Eng	*	*	£3	£17
1941 Scot	*	*	£4	£20
1942 Eng	*	*	*	£17
1942 Scot	*	*	*	£20
1943 Eng	*	*	*	£17
1943 Scot	*	*	*	£17
1944 Eng	*	*	*	£17
1944 Scot	*	*	*	£17
1945 Eng	*	*	*	£12
1945 Scot	*	*	*	£12

	F	VF	EF	Unc
1946 Eng	*	*	*	£11
1946 Scot	*	*	*	£11
1947 Eng	*	*	*	£9
1947 Scot	*	*	*	£9
1948 Eng	*	*	*	£9
1948 Scot	*	*	*	£9
1949 Eng	*	*	*	£27
1949 Scot	*	*	*	£27
1950 Eng	*	*	*	£27
1950 Eng proof	*	*	*	£27
1950 Scot	*	*	*	£27
1950 Scot proof	*	*	*	£27
1951 Eng	*	*	*	£27
1951 Eng proof	*	*	*	£27
1951 Scot	*	*	*	£27
1951 Scot proof	*	*	*	£27

ELIZABETH II

	F	VF	EF	Unc
1953 Eng	*	*	*	£6
1953 Eng proof	*	*	*	£11
1953 Scot	*	*	*	£6
1953 Scot proof	*	*	*	£11
1954 Eng	*	*	*	£6
1954 Scot	*	*	*	£6
1955 Eng	*	*	*	£6
1955 Scot	*	*	*	£6
1956 Eng	*	*	*	£11
1956 Scot	*	*	*	£10
1957 Eng	*	*	*	£5
1957 Scot	*	*	*	£22
1958 Eng	*	*	*	£55
1958 Scot	*	*	*	£5
1959 Eng	*	*	*	£5
1959 Scot	*	*	*	£80
1960 Eng	*	*	*	£2.50
1960 Scot	*	*	*	£4
1961 Eng	*	*	*	£2.50
1961 Scot	*	*	*	£11
1962 Eng	*	*	*	£1
1962 Scot	*	*	*	£1
1963 Eng	*	*	*	£1
1963 Scot	*	*	*	£1
1964 Eng	*	*	*	£1
1964 Scot	*	*	*	£1
1965 Eng	*	*	*	£1
1965 Scot	*	*	*	£1
1966 Eng	*	*	*	£1
1966 Scot	*	*	*	£1

■ SIXPENCES

CROMWELL

	F	VF	EF
1658		highest rarity	
1658 Dutch copy	*	£4500	£8000

CHARLES II

	F	VF	EF
1674	£70	£275	£800
1675	£75	£275	£800

	F	VF	EF
675/4	£70	£275	£800
676	£80	£290	£850
676/5	£80	£280	£850
677	£70	£250	£775
678/7	£70	£275	£800
679	£80	£280	£850
680	£80	£280	£850
681	£70	£270	£800
682	£80	£300	£900
682/1	£70	£270	£800
683	£70	£240	£775
684	£75	£270	£800

ABOVE: James II 1686 Sixpence

AMES II

686 early shields	£120	£375	£1700
687 early shields	£120	£375	£1700
687/6	£120	£375	£1700
687 later shields	£120	£375	£1700
687/6	£130	£390	£1850
688	£120	£375	£1700

WILLIAM AND MARY

693	£130	£400	£1350

ABOVE: William and Mary 1693 Sixpence

693 3 upside down	£140	£450	£1400
694	£160	£475	£1600

WILLIAM III

695 1st bust early hp	£35	£100	£390
696	£30	£80	£220
696 no obv stops	£50	£135	£475
696/5	£35	£110	£475
696 B	£35	£90	£375
696 C	£40	£110	£475
696 E	£40	£110	£475
696 N	£40	£110	£475
696 y	£35	£100	£450

	F	VF	EF
1696 Y	£45	£110	£450
1696 1st bust later hp	£55	£140	£475
1696 B	£80	£220	*
1696 C	£65	£240	£525
1696 N	£75	£250	£550
1696 2nd bust	£200	£600	£1750
1696 3rd bust, early hp, E			ext. rare
1696 3rd bust, early hp, y			ext. rare
1697 1st bust early hp	£30	£65	£280
1697 B	£45	£110	£450
1697 C	£65	£160	£525
1697 E	£45	£120	£450
1697 N	£45	£120	£450
1697 y	£45	£120	£450
1697 2nd bust	£150	£500	£1300
1697 3rd bust later hp	£30	£80	£270
1697 B	£45	£110	£450
1697 C	£65	£190	£675
1697 E	£65	£150	£525
1697 Y	£65	£170	£550
1698	£50	£100	£325
1698 plumes	£90	£220	£725
1699	£90	£220	£650
1699 plumes	£75	£200	£650
1699 roses	£90	£240	£725

ABOVE: William III 1699 plumes Sixpence

1700	£30	£65	£325
1700 plume below bust	£3300	*	*
1701	£50	£120	£475

ANNE

1703 VIGO	£50	£140	£425
1705	£65	£200	£600
1705 plumes	£60	£180	£550
1705 r&p	£65	£185	£525
1707	£45	£150	£440
1707 plain	£30	£80	£290
1707 E	£35	£110	£400
1707 plumes	£40	£120	£420

ABOVE: Anne 1707 plumes Sixpence

	F	VF	EF
1708 plain	£35	£110	£290
1708 E	£45	£125	£460
1708/7 E	£75	£180	£520
1708 E*	£45	£160	£520
1708/7 E*	£65	£190	£570
1708 Edin bust E*	£65	£220	£720
1708 plumes	£50	£130	£495
1710 r&p	£55	£145	£500
1711	£30	£85	£220

ABOVE: George I 1726 roses and plumes Sixpence

GEORGE I

	F	VF	EF
1717 r&p	£60	£210	£625
1720/17 r&p	£60	£190	£590
1723 SS C, small letters on obv	£40	£95	£275
1723 SS C, large letters on both sides	£40	£95	£275
1726 small r&p	£50	£225	£750

ABOVE: George II 1728 roses and plumes Sixpence

GEORGE II

	F	VF	EF
1728 YH	£70	£240	£625
1728 plumes	£60	£190	£525
1728 YH r&p	£60	£190	£525
1731	£40	£125	£420
1732	£40	£125	£420
1734	£45	£140	£490
1735	£45	£135	£470
1735/4	£40	£140	£495
1736	£40	£135	£430
1739 roses	£40	£120	£350
1739 O/R	£70	£200	£500
1741	£40	£120	£350
1743 OH roses	£40	£120	£350
1745	£25	£110	£325
1745/3	£45	£140	£375
1745 LIMA	£30	£90	£240
1746	£30	£90	£240
1746 plain proof	*	*	£2000

	F	VF	EF
1750	£40	£140	£350
1751	£45	£190	£425
1757	£15	£25	£70
1757	£15	£25	£70
1758/7	£20	£40	£80

GEORGE III	F	VF	EF	Unc
1787 hearts	£12	£25	£60	£135
1787 no hearts	£12	£25	£60	£135
1816	£9	£15	£65	£135
1817	£9	£15	£65	£135
1818	£10	£20	£80	£165
1819	£10	£20	£80	£175
1819/8	£10	£25	£90	£200
1819 small 8	£12	£25	£85	£180
1820	£10	£20	£75	£150
1820 1 inv	£60	£220	£550	*

GEORGE IV

	F	VF	EF	Unc
1820 1st head 1st rev pattern or proof	*	*	*	£5700
1821 proof	*	*	*	£1250
1821 BBITANNIAR error	£110	£300	£850	*
1824 1st head 2nd rev	£10	£30	£175	£400
1825	£10	£25	£160	£400
1826	£25	£95	£325	£650
1826 2nd head 3rd rev	£10	£25	£130	£325
1826 proof	*	*	*	£700
1827	£18	£60	£330	£700
1828	£10	£25	£230	£550
1829	£10	£25	£170	£440

ABOVE: William IV 1831 proof Sixpence

WILLIAM IV

	F	VF	EF	Unc
1831	£12	£25	£120	£275
1831 proof	*	*	*	£550
1834	£12	£35	£130	£300
1835	£12	£30	£130	£300
1836	£18	£40	£185	£340
1837	£15	£35	£180	£340

VICTORIA

	F	VF	EF	Unc
1838 1st YH	£10	£20	£120	£325
1839	£10	£20	£120	£325
1839 proof	*	*	*	£900
1840	£10	£20	£125	£325
1841	£10	£25	£160	£340
1842	£10	£25	£135	£325
1843	£10	£20	£130	£310

	F	VF	EF	Unc		F	VF	EF	Unc
1844	£10	£20	£130	£310	1883	£8	£12	£75	£130
1845	£10	£20	£130	£310	1884	£8	£12	£75	£140
1846	£10	£20	£130	£310	1885	£8	£12	£75	£140
1848	£35	£120	£480	£900	1886	£7	£12	£70	£140
1848/6	£30	£110	£440	£825	1887	£7	£12	£70	£140
1850	£15	£20	£135	£320	1887 JH shield rev	£5	£8	£12	£30
1850 5/3	£20	£50	£220	£425	1887 proof	*	*	*	£300
1851	£10	£20	£135	£320	1887 new rev	£5	£8	£14	£35
1852	£10	£20	£135	£320	1888	£5	£10	£35	£95
1853	£10	£20	£125	£285	1889	£5	£10	£35	£95
1853 proof	*	*	*	£1350	1890	*	£10	£45	£115
1854	£140	£420	£1000	*	1891	*	£12	£40	£110
1855	£10	£18	£130	£300	1892	*	£10	£50	£125
1855/3	£12	£20	£135	£310	1893	£270	£750	£2500	£4350
1856	£10	£18	£130	£300	1893 OH	*	£8	£25	£90
1857	£10	£18	£130	£300	1893 proof	*	*	*	£325
1858	£10	£18	£130	£300	1894	*	£9	£40	£115
1859	£10	£18	£130	£300	1895	*	£8	£35	£125
1859/8	£10	£22	£135	£310	1896	*	£8	£35	£110
1860	£10	£18	£130	£300	1897	*	£7	£35	£110
1862	£60	£120	£500	£1000	1898	*	£8	£40	£125
1863	£45	£90	£375	£800	1899	*	£8	£40	£125
1864	£10	£18	£120	£280	1900	*	£8	£40	£110
1865	£10	£18	£130	£300	1901	*	£8	£35	£110
1866	£10	£18	£130	£300					
1866 no die no				ext. rare	**EDWARD VII**				
1867	£12	£25	£135	£320	1902	*	£9	£45	£85
1868	£12	£25	£135	£320	1902 matt proof	*	*	*	£100
1869	£12	£30	£145	£340	1903	*	£12	£60	£125
1870	£15	£30	£160	£340	1904	*	£25	£110	£270
					1905	*	£25	£95	£230
					1906	*	£12	£55	£115
					1907	*	£12	£60	£125
					1908	*	£18	£65	£135
					1909	*	£12	£60	£125
					1910	*	£8	£45	£85

ABOVE: Victoria 1871 proof Sixpence

	F	VF	EF	Unc		F	VF	EF	Unc
					GEORGE V				
					1911	*	*	£23	£55
1871	£8	£15	£110	£300	1911 proof	*	*	*	£130
1871 no die no	£8	£18	£120	£320	1912	*	*	£32	£75
1872	£8	£18	£120	£320	1913	*	*	£38	£80
1873	£8	£15	£110	£300	1914	*	*	£20	£50
1874	£8	£15	£110	£270	1915	*	*	£25	£60
1875	£8	£15	£110	£290	1916	*	*	£20	£50
1876	£10	£25	£135	£340	1917	*	*	£45	£125
1877	£8	£15	£110	£285	1918	*	*	£20	£50
1877 no die no	£8	£15	£110	£285	1919	*	*	£25	£60
1878	£8	£15	£110	£285	1920	*	*	£28	£67
1878/7	£45	£125	£625	£1100	1920 debased	*	*	£28	£67
1878 DRITANNIAR error	£70	£195	£870	*	1921	*	*	£22	£72
1879 die no	£12	£25	£130	£320	1922	*	*	£22	£72
1879 no die no	£8	£15	£110	£285	1923	*	*	£25	£75
1880 2nd YH	£8	£15	£90	£245	1924	*	*	£20	£55
1880 3rd YH	£7	£15	£80	£130	1925	*	*	£20	£50
1881	£7	£12	£70	£120	1925 new rim	*	*	£18	£45
1882	£10	£30	£110	£290	1926	*	*	£18	£40
					1926 mod eff	*	*	£15	£32
					1927	*	*	£18	£40

	F	VF	EF	Unc
1927 new rev proof	*	*	*	£60
1928	*	*	£8	£27
1929	*	*	£8	£27
1930	*	*	£9	£30
1931	*	*	£9	£30
1932	*	*	£14	£50
1933	*	*	£9	£30
1934	*	*	£12	£45
1935	*	*	£6	£20
1936	*	*	£6	£20

GEORGE VI

	F	VF	EF	Unc
1937	*	*	£3	£11
1937 proof	*	*	*	£18
1938	*	*	£5	£22
1939	*	*	£3	£17
1940	*	*	£3	£22
1941	*	*	£3	£11
1942	*	*	£3	£11
1943	*	*	£3	£11
1944	*	*	£3	£11
1945	*	*	£3	£11
1946	*	*	£3	£11
1947	*	*	£1.50	£7.50
1948	*	*	£1.50	£7.50
1949	*	*	£1.50	£11
1950	*	*	£2	£13
1950 proof	*	*	*	£20
1951	*	*	£2	£16
1951 proof	*	*	*	£20
1952	*	£6	£22	£120

ELIZABETH II

	F	VF	EF	Unc
1953	*	*	*	£6
1953 proof	*	*	*	£7
1954	*	*	*	£6
1955	*	*	*	£4
1956	*	*	*	£4
1957	*	*	*	£4
1958	*	*	*	£7
1959	*	*	*	£3
1960	*	*	*	£5
1961	*	*	*	£5
1962	*	*	*	£1
1963	*	*	*	£1
1964	*	*	*	£1
1965	*	*	*	£1
1966	*	*	*	£1
1967	*	*	*	£1

◼ GROATS 'BRITANNIA' TYPE

Earlier dates are included in Maundy sets (see p134).

WILLIAM IV

	F	VF	EF	Unc
1836	*	*	£50	£110
1836 proof	*	*	*	£900
1837	*	*	£65	£130

VICTORIA	F	VF	EF	Unc
1837 proof	*	*	*	£1400
1838	*	£6	£45	£120
1838 8/8 on side	*	£18	£70	£175
1839	*	£9	£50	£130
1839 proof	*	*	*	£600
1840	*	£12	£45	£120
1840 narrow 0	*	£15	£50	*
1841	*	£12	£55	£135
1841 I for last 1	*	*	*	*
1842	*	£9	£55	£135
1842/1	*	£20	£75	£185
1843	*	£9	£55	£135
1843 4/5	*	£20	£75	£190
1844	*	£9	£55	£135
1845	*	£10	£60	£135
1846	*	£9	£55	£135
1847/6	£28	£75	£350	*
1848	*	£9	£50	£130
1848/6	£12	£30	£80	*
1848/7	*	£22	£95	£275
1849	*	£12	£50	£130
1849/8	*	£12	£55	£135
1851	£23	£100	£370	*
1852	£50	£190	£525	*

ABOVE: Victoria 1852 Groat

	F	VF	EF	Unc
1853	£50	£200	£485	*
1853 proof	*	*	*	£1300
1854	*	£9	£50	£130
1854 5/3	*	£25	£90	*
1855	*	£9	£50	£130
1857 proof	*	*	*	£1900
1862 proof	*	*	*	£2300
1888 JH	*	£22	£45	£95

◼ SILVER THREEPENCES

Earlier dates are included in Maundy sets.

WILLIAM IV

	F	VF	EF	Unc
1834	*	£14	£75	£200
1835	*	£14	£70	£185
1836	*	£14	£75	£200
1837	*	£25	£90	£220

ABOVE: Victoria 1866 Threepence

VICTORIA	F	VF	EF	Unc
1838	*	£18	£65	£185
1839	*	£22	£100	£230
1840	*	£20	£90	£230
1841	*	£20	£100	£220
1842	*	£20	£100	£220
1843	*	£18	£75	£175
1844	*	£18	£90	£210
1845	*	£15	£65	£140
1846	*	£65	£210	£430
1847	£50	£130	£410	£825
1848	£40	£110	£410	£775
1849	*	£18	£100	£195
1850	*	£10	£50	£200
1851	*	£15	£75	£170
1852	£50	£160	£470	*
1853	*	£55	£200	£395
1854	*	£12	£65	£160
1855	*	£18	£90	£190
1856	*	£12	£65	£160
1857	*	£18	£75	£185
1858	*	£15	£60	£175
1858 BRITANNIAB error		ext. rare		
1858/6	£12	£30	£170	£290
1859	*	£10	£55	£130
1860	*	£18	£100	£200
1861	*	£9	£70	£175
1862	*	£9	£55	£130
1863	*	£12	£90	£180
1864	*	£10	£55	£130
1865	*	£12	£75	£160
1866	*	£9	£55	£130
1867	*	£9	£55	£130
1868	*	£9	£55	£130
1868 RRITANNIAR error		ext. rare		
1869	£12	£35	£110	£260
1870	*	£7	£55	£130
1871	*	£8	£65	£130
1872	*	£6	£60	£130
1873	*	£6	£45	£100
1874	*	£5	£45	£95
1875	*	£6	£40	£95
1876	*	£6	£40	£95
1877	*	£6	£45	£110
1878	*	£6	£45	£110
1879	*	£6	£45	£110
1880	*	£6	£42	£95
1881	*	£6	£42	£85
1882	*	£10	£65	£130
1883	*	£6	£42	£85
1884	*	£6	£42	£85
1885	*	£6	£42	£85
1886	*	£6	£42	£85
1887 YH	*	£7	£45	£95
1887 JH	*	£3	£6	£17
1887 proof	*	*	*	£100
1888	*	£3	£15	£45
1889	*	£3	£12	£40
1890	*	£3	£12	£40
1891	*	£3	£12	£40

	F	VF	EF	Unc
1892	*	£4	£15	£45
1893	£25	£65	£150	£425
1893 OH	*	*	£15	£45
1893 proof	*	*	*	£130
1894	*	£3	£25	£55
1895	*	£3	£20	£50
1896	*	£2	£18	£45
1897	*	*	£15	£40
1898	*	*	£15	£40
1899	*	*	£15	£40
1900	*	*	£12	£35
1901	*	*	£12	£35
EDWARD VII				
1902	*	*	£12	£30
1902 matt proof	*	*	*	£35
1903	*	£3	£30	£55
1904	*	£7	£38	£110
1905	*	£7	£28	£80
1906	*	£6	£38	£100
1907	*	£3	£28	£55
1908	*	£3	£15	£55
1909	*	£3	£28	£65
1910	*	£3	£15	£40
GEORGE V				
1911	*	*	£7	£22
1911 proof	*	*	*	£40
1912	*	*	£7	£22
1913	*	*	£7	£22
1914	*	*	£5	£22
1915	*	*	£6	£27
1916	*	*	£4	£17
1917	*	*	£4	£17
1918	*	*	£4	£17
1919	*	*	£4	£17
1920	*	*	£4	£22
1920 debased	*	*	£4	£22
1921	*	*	£4	£22
1922	*	*	£16	£65
1925	*	£2	£15	£55
1926	*	£6	£37	£110
1926 mod eff	*	£2	£12	£45
1927 new rev proof	*	*	*	£100
1928	*	£3	£17	£50
1930	*	£2	£9	£32
1931	*	*	£3	£14
1932	*	*	£1.50	£10
1933	*	*	£1.50	£10
1934	*	*	£3	£14
1935	*	*	£3	£16
1936	*	*	£3	£14
GEORGE VI				
1937	*	*	£2.50	£6
1937 proof	*	*	*	£13
1938	*	*	£2.50	£6
1939	*	£1.50	£6	£22
1940	*	*	£2	£8

	F	VF	EF	Unc
1941	*	*	£3	£14
1942	*	£3	£7	£38
1943	*	£4	£19	£60
1944	*	£7	£30	£85
1945	*	*	*	*

Some of the Threepences were issued for use in the Colonies. Note: all specimens of 1945 were probably melted down but it appears that one or two still exist.

■ SMALL SILVER FOR COLONIES

These tiny coins were struck for issue in some of the Colonies but they were never issued for circulation in Britain. However, they are often included in collections of British coins, so we have given the prices.

Twopences

Other dates are included in Maundy sets.

VICTORIA	F	VF	EF	Unc
1838	*	£6	£25	£50
1838 2nd 8 like S	*	£10	£35	£80
1848	*	£6	£25	£55

Threehalfpences

WILLIAM IV				
1834	*	£6	£45	£95
1835	*	£6	£70	£170
1835/4	*	£12	£45	£120
1836	*	£6	£50	£10
1837	£12	£28	£110	£320

VICTORIA				
1838	*	£9	£30	£90
1839	*	£9	£30	£80
1840	*	£20	£70	£160
1841	*	£9	£32	£95
1842	*	£9	£32	£95
1843	*	£9	£25	£80
1843/34	£7	£22	£70	£160
1860	£5	£18	£50	£150
1862	£5	£18	£50	£150
1870 proof				£950

■ NICKEL–BRASS THREEPENCES

ABOVE: Edward VIII 1937 Threepence, extremely rare

The 1937 Edward VIII threepences, struck in 1936 ready for issue, were melted after Edward's abdication.

A few, however, escaped into circulation to become highly prized collectors' pieces.

George VI 1937 threepences were struck in large numbers, and are consequently worth much less.

EDWARD VIII	F	VF	EF	BU
1937	*	*	£35000	*

GEORGE VI	F	VF	EF	BU
1937	*	*	£1.50	£7
1938	*	*	£4	£30
1939	*	*	£7	£55
1940	*	*	£3	£23
1941	*	*	£1.50	£9
1942	*	*	£1.50	£9
1943	*	*	£1.50	£9
1944	*	*	£1.50	£9
1945	*	*	£3	£14
1946	*	£17	£195	£850
1948	*	*	£6	£50
1949	*	£17	£155	£725
1950	*	*	£17	£90
1951	*	*	£27	£120
1952	*	*	*	£14

ELIZABETH II				
1953	*	*	*	£5.50
1953 proof	*	*	*	£10
1954	*	*	*	£5.50
1955	*	*	*	£8
1956	*	*	*	£8
1957	*	*	*	£4.50
1958	*	*	*	£14
1959	*	*	*	£3.50
1960	*	*	*	£3.50
1961	*	*	*	£1
1962	*	*	*	£1
1963	*	*	*	£1
1964	*	*	*	£1
1965	*	*	*	£1
1966	*	*	*	£1
1967	*	*	*	*

■ COPPER TWOPENCE

GEORGE III				
1797	£25	£80	£385	£1250

■ COPPER PENNIES

GEORGE III				
1797 10 leaves	£8	£40	£260	£585
1797 11 leaves	£8	£50	£270	£590
1806	£4	£9	£95	£375
1806 no incuse curl	£4	£9	£95	£380
1807	£4	£9	£100	£395
1808 unique	*	*	*	£130000

ABOVE: George III 1806 Penny

GEORGE IV

	F	VF	EF	BU
1825	£7	£28	£185	£700
1826	£7	£15	£165	£625
1826 proof	*	*	£325	£875
1826 thin line down St Andrew's cross	£8	£27	£185	£650
1826 thick line	£10	£45	£240	*
1827	£375	£800	£4500	*

ABOVE: William IV 1831

WILLIAM IV

	F	VF	EF	BU
1831	£12	£55	£295	£1100
1831 proof	*	*	*	£1100
1831 .ww inc				ext. rare
1831 w.w inc	£18	£80	£385	*
1834	£18	£80	£385	£1400
1837	£22	£905	£625	£2100

ABOVE: Victoria 1841 Penny

VICTORIA

	F	VF	EF	BU
1839 proof	*	*	*	£2200
1841	£22	£65	£325	£825
1841 no colon after REG	£5	£18	£70	£395
1843	£95	£325	£1700	£4000
1843 no colon after REG	£70	£210	£1400	£3650
1844	£5	£22	£110	£490
1845	£10	£25	£150	£750
1846 DEF far colon	£4	£18	£120	£500
1846 DEF close colon	£4	£19	£140	£500
1847 DEF close colon	£4	£18	£100	£390
1847 DEF far colon	£4	£18	£100	£360
1848	£4	£15	£95	£425
1848/6	£18	£80	£480	*
1848/7	£4	£18	£100	£420
1849	£110	£425	£1550	£3600
1851 DEF far colon	£4	£20	£130	£480
1851 DEF close colon	£5	£18	£120	£470
1853 OT	£3	£12	£90	£300
1853 proof	*	*	*	£2700
1853 PT	£3	£12	£95	£350
1854 PT	£3	£12	£90	£275
1854/3	£18	£45	£175	£490
1854 OT	£3	£12	£90	£300
1855 OT	£3	£12	£90	£300
1855 PT	£3	£12	£90	£300
1856 PT	£55	£170	£750	£2100
1856 OT	£65	£210	£900	£2650
1857 OT	£3	£12	£90	£330
1857 PT	£3	£12	£90	£310
1857 small date	£3	£12	£95	£330
1858	£3	£12	£70	£260
1858 small date	£4	£14	£95	£335
1858/3	£4	£14	£95	£335
1858/7	£4	£7	£85	£370
1858 no ww	£4	£7	£85	£295
1858 no ww (large 1 and 5, small 8s)	£4	£9	£70	£295
1859	£4	£12	£100	£420
1859 small date	£5	£18	£120	£430
1860/59	£350	£925	£3300	*

■ BRONZE PENNIES

For fuller details of varieties in bronze pennies see *English Copper, Tin and Bronze Coins in the British Museum 1558–1958* by C W Peck, *The Bronze Coinage of Great Britain* by M J Freeman and *The British Bronze Penny 1860–1970* by Michael Gouby.

The die pairings below are from Gouby, a must for the penny collector. There are many varieties and die combinations, and only the more significant are listed below.

VICTORIA	F	VF	EF	BU
1860 BB, dies C/a	£110	£320	£725	*
1860 BB dies C/b	£45	£110	£250	£550
1860 BB rev rock to left of lighthouse, dies C/c	£85	£220	£800	*
1860 obv BB/rev TB, dies C/d	£425	£775	£1600	£3200

ABOVE: Victoria 1860 bronze Penny

	F	VF	EF	BU
1860 obv TB/rev BB, dies D/b	£320	£650	£2300	£6250
1860 TB, signature on cape, dies D/d	*	£17	£65	£240
1860 TB, rev L.C.W. inc below foot, dies E/e	£325	£600	£1100	£2900
1860 TB, rev L.C.W inc below shield, dies F/d	*	£18	£95	£230
1860 TB obv, no signature on cape, dies H/d	*	£160	£420	£825

ABOVE: 1861 bronze Penny

	F	VF	EF	BU
1861 signature on cape, rev LCW below shield, dies D/d	£85	£230	£460	£1600
1861 signature on cape, rev no signature, dies D/g	£85	£360	£460	£1600
1861 signature below cape, L.C.W. below shield, dies F/d	*	£12	£95	£320
1861 signature below cape, rev no signature, dies F/g	£85	£360	£870	*
1861 obv no signature, L.C.W. below shield, dies H/d	*	£22	£110	£320
1861 date: 6 over 8	£425	£1300	£2900	*
1861 no signature either side, dies J/g	*	£15	£80	£285
1862 obv signature, rev no LCW, dies D/g	£470	£900	£2100	*
1862 obv no signature dies J/g	*	£12	£80	£280
1862 date: small figures (½d size)	£500	£1600	£4200	*
1863 dies J/g	*	£11	£65	£210

	F	VF	EF	BU
1863 die no 2 below date	£2000	*	*	*
1863 die no 3 below date	£1900	£3300	*	*
1863 die no 4 below date	£2600	*	*	*
1863 die no 5 below date	£20,000	*	*	*
1864 upper serif to 4 in date	£22	£170	£1700	£4200
1864 crosslet serif to 4 in date	£30	£200	£2000	£4850
1865	*	£30	£160	£535
1865/3	£45	£130	£550	£1750
1866	*	£17	£95	£440
1867	£12	£38	£265	£775
1868	£12	£45	£290	£950
1869	£165	£470	£3000	£6700
1870	£12	£45	£270	£625
1871	£33	£90	£850	£1900
1872	*	£15	£90	£325
1873	*	£15	£90	£360
1874	*	£23	£130	£420
1874 H dies J/g	*	£15	£90	£335
1874 rev lighthouse tall and thin, dies J/j	£22	£100	£320	£620
1874 H dies J/j	£28	£100	£265	£675
1874 obv, aged portrait, dies K/g	*	£22	£90	£335
1874 H	*	£22	£90	£335
1875 dies L/k	*	£18	£85	£295
1875 H	£33	£220	£950	£2600
1876 H	*	£18	£90	£285
1877	*	£10	£80	£325
1878	*	£40	£180	£525
1879	*	*	£80	£220
1880 no rock to left of lighthouse, dies M/k	£15	£38	£130	£385
1880 rocks to left of lighthouse, dies M/n	£15	£50	£165	£525
1881	*	*	£210	£590
1881 new obv, dies P/k	£50	£150	£365	*
1881 H	*	*	£70	£290
1882 H	*	*	£70	£245
1882 no H	£900	£2650	*	*
1883	*	*	£65	£230
1884	*	*	£55	£170
1885	*	*	£55	£170
1886	*	*	£55	£170
1887	*	*	£50	£145
1888	*	*	£55	£170
1889 14 leaves	*	*	£50	£145
1889 15 leaves	*	*	£55	£170
1890	*	*	£45	£130
1891	*	*	£45	£130
1892	*	*	£45	£150
1893	*	*	£45	£130
1894	*	*	£65	£235
1895 2mm	*	£55	£370	£1600

	F	VF	EF	BU		F	VF	EF	BU
1895	*	*	£18	£80	1929	*	*	£15	£40
1896	*	*	£15	£75	1930	*	*	£25	£60
1897	*	*	£15	£75	1931	*	*	£18	£50
1897 higher horizon	£45	£130	£625	*	1932	*	*	£33	£130
1898	*	*	£17	£80	1933			highest rarity	
1899	*	*	£17	£75	1934	*	*	£18	£45
1900	*	*	£15	£60	1935	*	*	£5	£17
1901	*	*	£12	£45	1936	*	*	£5	£17

EDWARD VII

	F	VF	EF	BU
1902 low horizon	*	£17	£110	£300
1902	*	*	£12	£50
1903	*	*	£23	£90
1904	*	*	£38	£160
1905	*	*	£38	£120
1906	*	*	£28	£110
1907	*	*	£28	£110
1908	*	*	£20	£95
1909	*	*	£28	£110
1910	*	*	£22	£95

ABOVE: Edward VIII proof Penny

EDWARD VIII

Proof penny			highest rarity	

GEORGE VI

	F	VF	EF	BU
1937	*	*	*	£6
1938	*	*	*	£6
1939	*	*	£1.50	£7
1940	*	*	£8	£50
1944	*	*	£6	£50
1945	*	*	£5	£22
1946	*	*	*	£11
1947	*	*	*	£8
1948	*	*	*	£8
1949	*	*	*	£8
1950	*	£8	£35	£65
1951	*	£8	£32	£50
1952 proof				unique

ABOVE: George V 1933 Penny

GEORGE V

	F	VF	EF	BU
1911	*	*	£15	£55
1912	*	*	£15	£65
1912 H	*	*	£60	£190
1913	*	*	£22	£80
1914	*	*	£20	£60
1915	*	*	£20	£60
1916	*	*	£20	£60
1917	*	*	£20	£60
1918	*	*	£20	£60
1918 H	*	£37	£275	£725
1918 KN	*	£50	£415	£1100
1919	*	*	£20	£65
1919 H	*	£50	£335	£950
1919 KN	*	£80	£750	£2300
1920	*	*	£18	£55
1921	*	*	£18	£55
1922	*	*	£18	£55
1922 rev as 1927		ext. rare		
1926	*	*	£33	£110
1926 mod eff	£28	£230	£1250	£3850
1927	*	*	£15	£40
1928	*	*	£15	£40

ABOVE: George VI 1952 Penny, unique

	F	VF	EF	BU
ELIZABETH II				
1953	*	£1	£5	£22
1953 proof	*	*	*	£23
1954		unique		
1961	*	*	*	£2.50
1962	*	*	*	£1
1963	*	*	*	£1
1964	*	*	*	£0.50
1965	*	*	*	£0.50
1966	*	*	*	£0.50
1967	*	*	*	£0.25

■ COPPER OR TIN HALFPENNIES

ABOVE: Charles II 1675 Halfpenny

CHARLES II	Fair	F	VF	EF
1672	£10	£50	£230	£1400
1672 CRAOLVS error		ext. rare		*
1673	£10	£50	£23	£1400
1673 CRAOLVS error		ext. rare		*
1673 no stops on rev	£13	£70	£340	*
1673 no stops on obv	£14	£70	£325	*
1675	£12	£55	£220	£1500
1675 no stops on obv	£12	£65	£320	*
1675 5/3	£40	£125	£425	*
JAMES II				
1685 tin	£70	£270	£675	£4700
1686 tin	£75	£270	£675	*
1687 tin	£70	£270	£625	*
1687 D/D	*	*	*	*
WILLIAM AND MARY				
1689 tin, ET on right	£670	£1300	£2650	*
1689 tin, ET on left	*	*	*	*
1690 tin, date on edge	£70	£210	£670	£3650
1691 tin, date in exergue and on edge	£70	£210	£670	£3650
1691/2 tin, 1691 in exergue 1692 on edge		ext. rare		*

	Fair	F	VF	EF
1692 tin, date in exergue and on edge	£75	£85	£475	*
1694 copper	£30	£60	£270	£1400
1694 GVLIEMVS error	£165	*	*	*
1694 no stop after MARIA	£28	£70	£325	£1450
1694 BRITANNIA with last I/A	£35	£130	£370	*
1694 no stop on rev	£25	£65	£325	£1400

ABOVE: William III 1696 Halfpenny

WILLIAM III

Type 1, date in exergue

1695	£12	£40	£190	£1400
1695 BRITANNIA, As unbarred	£55	£180	*	*
1695 no stop on rev	£12	£55	£230	*
1696	£12	£40	£185	£1400
1696 GVLIEMVS, no stop on rev		ext. rare		*
1696 TERTVS error	£90	£220	*	*
1697	£12	£50	£185	£1400
1697 no stops	£40	£160	*	*
1697 I/E on TERTIVS	£40	£160	*	*
1697 GVLILMVS no stop on rev		ext. rare		*
1697 no stop after TERTIVS	£18	£45	£165	£1400
1698	£18	£50	£220	*

Type 2, date in legend

1698	£12	£50	£235	£1400
1699	£12	£35	£230	£1300
1699 BRITANNIA, As unbarred	£40	£170	*	*
1699 GVLIEMVS error	£40	£170	*	*

Type 3, Britannia's hand on knee, date in exergue

1699	£12	£35	£220	£1300
1699 stop after date	£40	£160	*	*
1699 BRITANNIA, As unbarred	£22	£75	£270	*
1699 GVILELMVS	£55	£235	*	*
1699 TERTVS	£55	£235	*	*
1699 no stop on rev	£40	£165	*	*
1699 no stops on obv	£18	£65	£270	*
1699 no stops after				

	Fair	F	VF	EF
GVLIELMVS	£17	£65	£275	*
1700	£10	£25	£215	£1300
1700 no stops on obv	£22	£75	£275	*
1700 no stops after GVLIELMVS	£22	£705	£275	*
1700 BRITANNIA, As unbarred	£10	£23	£215	£1300
1700 no stop on reverse	£10	£28	£220	£1300
1700 GVLIELMS error	£22	£75	£270	*
1700 GVLIEEMVS error	£15	£50	£190	*
1700 TER TIVS error	£10	£22	£215	£1300
1700 I/V on TERTIVS	£55	£230	*	*
1701 BRITANNIA, As unbarred	£10	£22	£210	£1300
1701 no stops on obv	£55	£230	*	*
1701 GVLIELMVS TERTIVS, Vs inverted As	£15	£50	£235	*

GEORGE I
Type 1

	Fair	F	VF	EF
1717	£12	£40	£270	£900
1717 no stops on obv	£18	£70	£500	*

ABOVE: George I 1717 Halfpenny

	Fair	F	VF	EF
1718	£12	£33	£235	£825
1718 no stop on obv	£18	£70	£500	*
1719 on large flan of type 2	£270	*	*	*
1719 on large flan of type 2, edge grained			ext. rare	*

Type 2

	Fair	F	VF	EF
1719 both shoulder straps ornate	£7	£28	£165	£850
1719 both shoulder straps ornate, edge grained			ext. rare	*
1719 bust with left strap plain	£7	£28	£165	£825
1720	£7	£28	£165	£775
1721	£7	£28	£165	£750
1721/0	£7	£28	£165	£750
1721 stop after date	£7	£28	£165	£750
1722	£7	£28	£165	£750
1722 GEORGIVS, V inverted A	£18	£95	£325	*
1723	£7	£28	£165	£750
1723 no stop on reverse	£18	£95	£325	*
1724	£7	£28	£165	£675

ABOVE: George II 1733 Halfpenny

GEORGE II
Young Head

	Fair	F	VF	EF
1729	*	£23	£90	£425
1729 no stop on rev	*	£28	£95	£450
1730	*	£23	£90	£400
1730 GEOGIVS, no stop on reverse	*	£28	£120	£475
1730 stop after date	£6	£22	£90	£400
1730 no stop after REX or on rev	*	£28	£120	£470
1731	*	£23	£90	£375
1731 rev no stop	*	£28	£110	£420
1732	*	£24	£85	£370
1732 rev no stop	*	£28	£110	£420
1733	*	£20	£75	£360
1734	*	£20	£75	£360
1734/3	*	£30	£160	*
1734 no stops on obv	*	£30	£160	*
1735	*	£20	£80	£360
1736	*	£20	£80	£360
1737	*	£20	£80	£360
1738	*	£20	£75	£340
1739	*	£20	£75	£340

Old Head

	Fair	F	VF	EF
1740	*	£8	£60	£290
1742	*	£8	£60	£290
1742/0	*	£12	£60	£290
1743	*	£8	£60	£290
1744	*	£8	£60	£290
1745	*	£8	£60	£290
1746	*	£8	£60	£290
1747	*	£8	£60	£290
1748	*	£8	£60	£290
1749	*	£8	£60	£290
1750	*	£8	£65	£310
1751	*	£8	£60	£290
	Fair	F	VF	EF
1752	*	£8	£60	£290
1753	*	£8	£60	£290
1754	*	£8	£60	£290

ABOVE: George II 1777 Halfpenny

	F	VF	EF	BU
1841	£4	£9	£55	£275
1843	£17	£50	£200	£725
1844	£8	£22	£120	£310
1845	£135	£370	£1500	*
1846	£9	£23	£100	£310
1847	£9	£23	£100	£310
1848	£22	£60	£185	£500
1848/7	£6	£22	£100	£320
1851	£4	£9	£55	£275
1851 seven inc dots on and above shield	£3	£6	£40	£250
1852	£4	£9	£55	£260
1852 seven inc dots on and above shield	£3	£9	£505	£225
1853 proof	*	*	*	£900
1853/2	£5	£30	£120	£320
1854	£4	£6	£50	£145

GEORGE III	F	VF	EF	BU
1770	£6	£50	£220	£790
1770 Proof	*	*	*	£2000
1771	£6	£50	£210	£790
1771 no stop on rev	£8	£50	£210	£790
1771 ball below spear head	£6	£50	£210	£790
1772	£6	£50	£210	£790
1772 GEORIVS error	£12	£85	£280	*
1772 ball below spear head	£6	£50	£210	£790
1772 no stop on rev	£6	£50	£210	£790
1773	£6	£50	£210	£790
1773 no stop after REX	£6	£50	£210	£790
1773 no stop on reverse	£6	£50	£210	*
1774	£6	£50	£210	£790
1775	£6	£50	£210	£860
1799 five inc gunports	*	£9	£65	£180
1799 six relief gunports	*	£9	£65	£180
1799 nine relief gunports	*	£9	£65	£210
1799 no gunports	*	£9	£65	£190
1799 no gunports and raised line along hull	*	£9	£65	£190
1806 no berries on olive branch	*	£9	£65	£180
1806 line under SOHO three berries	*	£9	£60	£180
1807	*	£9	£60	£180

GEORGE IV				
1825	*	£33	£140	£360
1826 Proof	*	*	*	£400
1826 two inc lines down cross	*	£18	£90	£265
1826 raised line down centre of cross	*	£22	£110	£285
1826 proof	*	*	*	£500
1827	*	£17	£90	£265

WILLIAM IV				
1831	*	£22	£120	£335
1831 Proof	*	*	*	£550
1834	*	£22	£120	£335
1837	*	£17	£110	£360

VICTORIA				
1838	£4	£9	£55	£275
1839 proof	*	*	*	£550
1839 proof, rev inv	*	*	*	£550

ABOVE: Victoria 1853 proof Halfpenny

	F	VF	EF	BU
1855	£3	£6	£50	£165
1856	£4	£10	£55	£260
1857	£3	£15	£50	£160
1857 seven inc dots on and above shield	£2	£6	£38	£140
1858	£3	£6	£50	£145
1858/6	£4	£12	£55	£160
1858/7	£3	£6	£50	£160
1858 small date	£2	£6	£40	£160
1859	£3	£6	£55	£190
1859/8	£7	£14	£100	£300
1860 proof only	*	*	*	£11000

■ BRONZE HALFPENNIES

For fuller details of varieties in bronze Halfpennies and Farthings see *English Copper, Tin and Bronze Coins in the British Museum 1558–1958* by C W Peck and *The Bronze Coinage of Great Britain* by M J Freeman. There is a large number of varieties and die combinations for this series, only the more significant are listed below.

VICTORIA	F	VF	EF	BU
1860 BB	*	£6	£45	£150
1860 rev TB/obv BB		ext. rare		*
1860 TB, 4 berries	*	£7	£60	£210
1860 TB, double				

ABOVE: Victoria 1860 bronze Halfpenny

	F	VF	EF	BU
inc leaf veins	*	£17	£95	£335
1861 obv 5 berries	*	£35	£120	£360
1861 obv 4 berries, rev L.C.W. on rock	*	£28	£120	£360
1861 rev no signature	£15	£55	£170	*
1861 rev no signature, breastplate has inc lines	*	£35	£110	£330
1861 obv 4 double incuse leaf veins, rev no signature, breastplate has inc lines	*	£22	£100	£275
1861 same obv, rev L.C.W. on rock	*	£7	£65	£210
1861 obv 7 double incuse leaf veins, rev L.C.W. on rock	*	£7	£65	£210
1861 rev no signature	*	£6	£45	£165
1861 obv 16 leaves, rev rounded to top lighthouse	*	£22	£100	£265
1861 rev pointed top to lighthouse	*	£6	£58	£270
1861 no signature	*	£7	£65	£210
1861 HALP error	£235	£600	*	*
1861 6/8	£220	£595	*	*
1862	*	£6	£38	£170
1862 letter A left of lighthouse base	£520	£770	£2100	*
1862 letter B left of lighthouse base	£900	£1600	£4600	*
1862 letter C left of lighthouse base	£825	*	*	*
1863	*	£6	£80	£250
1864	*	£7	£80	£310
1865	*	£12	£110	£470
1865/3	£33	£95	£360	£850
1866	*	£9	£75	£320
1867	*	£9	£90	£395
1868	*	£9	£85	£320
1869	£22	£70	£365	£1250
1870	*	£6	£80	£250
1871	£22	£70	£365	£1000
1872	*	£6	£60	£185
1873	*	£9	£80	£255
1874	*	£22	£130	£460
1874 H	*	£6	£55	£190
1875	*	£7	£60	£190
1875 H	*	£7	£80	£250
1876 H	*	£6	£55	£190
1877	*	£6	£55	£190

	F	VF	EF	BU
1878	*	£20	£120	£435
1879	*	£6	£50	£175
1880	*	£5	£50	£190
1881	*	£5	£50	£190
1881 H	*	£5	£50	£190
1882 H	*	£5	£50	£190
1883	*	£5	£50	£190
1884	*	£3	£50	£175
1885	*	*	£50	£175
1886	*	*	£50	£175
1887	*	*	£50	£175
1888	*	*	£50	£175
1889	*	*	£50	£175
1889/8	*	£22	£120	£335
1890	*	*	£45	£150
1891	*	*	£45	£150
1892	*	*	£45	£150
1893	*	*	£45	£150
1894	*	£6	£65	£210
1895 OH	*	*	£15	£75
1896	*	*	£12	£70
1897 normal horizon	*	*	£12	£70
1897 higher horizon	*	*	£12	£70
1898	*	*	£12	£70
1899	*	*	£12	£70
1900	*	*	£6	£45
1901	*	*	£5	£40
EDWARD VII				
1902 low horizon	*	£38	£140	£385
1902	*	*	£12	£40
1903	*	*	£17	£100
1904	*	*	£22	£140
1905	*	*	£19	£105
1906	*	*	£19	£105
1907	*	*	£15	£90
1908	*	*	£15	£90
1909	*	*	£19	£100
1910	*	*	£15	£80
GEORGE V				
1911	*	*	£9	£40
1912	*	*	£10	£50
1913	*	*	£10	£50
1914	*	*	£12	£55
1915	*	*	£12	£55
1916	*	*	£12	£55
1917	*	*	£7	£40
1918	*	*	£7	£40
1919	*	*	£6	£40
1920	*	*	£8	£50
1921	*	*	£8	£45
1922	*	*	£17	£65
1923	*	*	£8	£50
1924	*	*	£8	£50
1925	*	*	£8	£50
1925 mod eff	*	*	£17	£60
1926	*	*	£8	£50
1927	*	*	£6	£38

	F	VF	EF	BU
1928	*	*	£6	£30
1929	*	*	£6	£32
1930	*	*	£6	£36
1931	*	*	£6	£32
1932	*	*	£17	£140
1933	*	*	£6	£33
1934	*	*	£17	£120
1935	*	*	£6	£32
1936	*	*	£5	£24

GEORGE VI

	F	VF	EF	BU
1937	*	*	*	£6
1937 proof	*	*	*	£14
1938	*	*	*	£10
1939	*	*	*	£24
1940	*	*	*	£24
1941	*	*	*	£10
1942	*	*	*	£7
1943	*	*	*	£7
1944	*	*	*	£7
1945	*	*	*	£9
1946	*	*	*	£20
1947	*	*	*	£7
1948	*	*	*	£7
1949	*	*	*	£17
1950	*	*	*	£14
1950 proof	*	*	*	£16
1951	*	*	*	£16
1951 proof	*	*	*	£16
1952	*	*	*	£9

ELIZABETH II

	F	VF	EF	BU
1953	*	*	*	£3
1953 proof	*	*	*	£8
1954	*	*	*	£6
1955	*	*	*	£5
1956	*	*	*	£6
1957	*	*	*	£2.50
1958	*	*	*	£2.50
1959	*	*	*	£1.25
1960	*	*	*	£1.25
1962	*	*	*	*
1963	*	*	*	*
1964	*	*	*	*
1965	*	*	*	*
1966	*	*	*	*
1967	*	*	*	*

COPPER FARTHINGS

OLIVER CROMWELL	Fair	F	VF	EF
Patterns only	*	£2950	£5850	£9500

CHARLES II				
1671 patterns only	*	*	£375	£800
1672	£3	£38	£185	£700
1672 no stop on obv	£6	£50	£260	£775
1672 loose drapery				

	Fair	F	VF	EF
at Britannia's elbow	£5	£38	£210	£800
1673	£3	£38	£185	£670
1673 CAROLA error	£33	£130	£470	*
1673 BRITINNIA error		ext. rare		
1673 no stops on obv	£33	£130	*	*
1673 rev no stop	£28	£130	*	*
1674	*	£38	£185	£750
1675	*	£38	£185	£700
1675 no stop after CAROLVS	£50	£170	*	*
1679	*	£28	£185	£800
1679 no stop on rev	£8	£80	£320	*
1694 tin, various edge readings	£38	£185	£570	£3200
1685 tin		ext. rare	*	*

ABOVE: James II 1685 tin Farthing

JAMES II

	Fair	F	VF	EF
1684 tin		ext. rare		*
1685 tin, various edge readings	£65	£170	£625	£2750
1686 tin, various edge readings	£80	£190	£650	£3200
1687 tin, draped bust, various readings		ext. rare	*	*

WILLIAM AND MARY

	Fair	F	VF	EF
1689 tin, date in exergue and on edge, many varieties	£265	£525	*	*
1689/90 tin, 1689 in exergue, 1690 on edge	*	*	*	*
1689/90 tin, 1690 in exergue, 1689 on edge	*	*	*	*
1690 tin, various types	£45	£165	£500	£2750
1691 tin, small and large figures	£45	£165	£500	£2750
1692 tin	£45	£165	£500	£2750
1694 copper, many varieties	£12	£55	£175	£825

ABOVE: William and Mary 1694 Farthing

WILLIAM III	Fair	F	VF	EF
Type 1, date in exergue				
1695	£3	£45	£170	£750
1695 GVLIELMV error	£65	£190	*	*
1696	*	£45	£155	£725
1697	*	£45	£155	£725
1698	£55	£180	£470	*
1699	£3	£45	£155	£725
1700	£3	£50	£155	£725
Type 2, date in legend				
1698	£6	£50	£185	£775
1699	£6	£50	£190	£785
ANNE				
1714 patterns F	*	*	£500	£900

ABOVE: George I 1717 'dump' Farthing

GEORGE I				
Smaller flan, 'dump type'				
1717	*	£165	£400	£900
1718		unique		
1718 silver proof	*	*	*	£3200
Larger flan				
1719 large lettering on obv	£4	£40	£220	£625
1719 small lettering on obv	£4	£40	£2025	£635
1719 last A over I in BRITANNIA	£12	£65	£310	*

ABOVE: George I 1721 Farthing

	Fair	F	VF	EF
1719 legend continuous over bust	£22	£65	*	*
1720 large lettering on obv	£22	£65	£285	*
1720 small lettering on obv	£3	£22	£115	£535
1721	£3	£22	£115	£535
1721/0	£6	£45	£135	£550
1722 large lettering on obv	*	£30	£135	£560
1722 small lettering on obv	*	£22	£115	£520

	Fair	F	VF	EF
1723	*	£22	£130	£535
1723 R/R REX	£15	£80	£160	£670
1724	£6	£28	£135	£570
GEORGE II				
1730	*	£12	£60	£320
1731	*	£12	£60	£320
1732	*	£15	£65	£360
1733	*	£12	£55	£320
1734	*	£12	£65	£360
1734 no stops on obv	*	£15	£75	£420
1735	*	£12	£45	£310
1735 3/3	*	£15	£75	£420
1736	*	£12	£55	£320
1736 triple tie-riband	*	£17	£75	£420
1737 small date	*	£12	£50	£310
1737 large date	*	£12	£50	£310
1739	*	£12	£50	£310
1739/5	*	£15	£60	£385
1741 OH	*	£12	£50	£230
1744	*	£12	£60	£275
1746	*	£12	£50	£235
1746 V/U		ext. rare	*	*
1749	*	£12	£50	£210
1750	*	£12	£60	£265
1754/0	*	£25	£90	£385
1754	*	£9	£45	£175

GEORGE III	F	VF	EF	BU
1771	£6	£50	£210	£420
1773	£6	£35	£180	£420
1774	£6	£35	£180	£420
1775	£6	£35	£180	£420
1799	*	*	£55	£130
1806	*	£4	£55	£130
1807	*	£4	£60	£140

GEORGE IV				
1821	*	£9	£50	£140
1822	*	£9	£50	£140
1823	*	£9	£50	£140
1825	*	£9	£50	£140
1825 D/U in DEI	*	£55	£185	*
1826 date on rev	*	£12	£65	£60
1826 date on obv	*	£10	£55	£145
1826 I for 1 in date	£18	£70	£320	£600
1826 proof	*	*	*	£350
1827	*	£10	£55	£150
1828	*	£10	£65	£150
1829	*	£12	£70	£190
1830	*	£10	£55	£145

WILLIAM IV				
1831	*	£8	£60	£165
1831 proof	*	*	*	£425
1834	*	£8	£60	£170
1835	*	£8	£60	£170
1836	*	£8	£60	£170
1837	*	£8	£60	£170

VICTORIA

	F	VF	EF	BU
1838	*	£6	£40	£170
1839	*	£6	£40	£160
1839 proof	*	*	*	£525
1840	*	£6	£40	£160
1841	*	£6	£40	£160
1842	*	£40	£110	£365
1843	*	£8	£45	£165
1843 I for 1	£45	£210	£590	*
1844	£40	£210	£620	£2200
1845	*	£7	£35	£155
1846	*	£7	£65	£175
1847	*	£6	£45	£150
1848	*	£7	£45	£150
1849	*	£55	£350	*
1850	*	£6	£40	£150
1851	*	£18	£55	£175
1851 D/D sideways	£12	£80	£320	£900
1852	*	£15	£60	£175
1853 proof	*	*	*	£850
1853 w.w. raised	*	£6	£40	£135
1853 w.w. inc	*	£22	£90	£300
1854	*	£6	£40	£110
1855	*	£7	£50	£150
1855 w.w. raised	*	£7	£45	£150
1856 w.w. inc	*	£8	£60	£175
1856 R/E in VICTORIA		£12	£55	£290
1857	*	£6	£45	£135
1858	*	£6	£45	£135
1859	*	£18	£55	£210
1860 proof	*	*	*	£9000

ABOVE: Victoria 1859 copper Farthing

BRONZE FARTHINGS

VICTORIA

	F	VF	EF	BU
1860 BB	*	£3	£22	£90
1860 TB/BB (mule)	£110	£220	£500	*
1860 TB	*	£2	£18	£80
1861	*	£2	£18	£70
1862 small 8	*	£2	£15	£70
1862 large 8	£45	£110	£235	*
1863	£25	£45	£165	£410
1864	*	£4	£35	£120
1865	*	£4	£30	£90
1865–5/2	*	£6	£40	£145
1866	*	£3	£23	£90
1867	*	£4	£33	£105
1868	*	£4	£33	£105

	F	VF	EF	BU
1869	*	£9	£45	£130
1872	*	£3	£22	£85
1873	*	£4	£22	£85
1874 H	*	£6	£35	£95
1874 H G sideways/Gs	£70	£180	£490	*
1875 large date	*	£12	£38	£130
1875 small date	£9	£22	£95	£320
1875 older features	*	£22	£85	£270
1875 H	*	£3	£17	£75
1875 H older features	£65	£180	£320	*
1876 H	*	£12	£40	£130
1877 proof only				£6500
1878	*	£3	£12	£80
1879	*	£3	£22	£85
1879 large 9	*	£2	£15	£95
1880	*	£3	£30	£105
1881	*	£6	£22	£80
1881 H	*	£3	£22	£80
1882 H	*	£3	£22	£80
1883	*	£6	£40	£120
1884	*	*	£15	£55
1885	*	*	£15	£55
1886	*	*	£15	£55
1887	*	*	£25	£80
1888	*	*	£15	£55
1890	*	*	£15	£60
1891	*	*	£15	£60
1892	*	£18	£65	£210
1893	*	*	£15	£65
1894	*	*	£15	£75
1895	*	£15	£60	£200
1895 OH	*	*	£4	£30
1896	*	*	£6	£33
1897 bright finish	*	*	£4	£33
1897 black finish higher horizon	*	*	£3	£33
1898	*	*	£4	£33
1899	*	*	£3	£33
1900	*	*	£3	£33
1901	*	*	£3	£17

EDWARD VII

	F	VF	EF	BU
1902	*	*	£4	£22
1903 low horizon	*	*	£5	£24
1904	*	*	£5	£22
1905	*	*	£5	£22
1906	*	*	£5	£22
1907	*	*	£5	£22
1908	*	*	£5	£22
1909	*	*	£5	£22
1910	*	*	£9	£28

GEORGE V

	F	VF	EF	BU
1911	*	*	£5	£17
1912	*	*	£5	£17
1913	*	*	£5	£17
1914	*	*	£5	£17
1915	*	*	£5	£17
1916	*	*	£5	£17

	F	VF	EF	BU
1917	*	*	£5	£12
1918 black finish	*	*	£7	£22
1919 bright finish	*	*	£4	£10
1919	*	*	£4	£12
1920	*	*	£4	£12
1921	*	*	£4	£12
1922	*	*	£4	£12
1923	*	*	£4	£12
1924	*	*	£4	£12
1925	*	*	£4	£12
1926 mod eff	*	*	£3	£9
1927	*	*	£3	£7
1928	*	*	*	£3.50
1929	*	*	*	£3.50
1930	*	*	*	£3.50
1931	*	*	*	£3.50
1932	*	*	*	£3.50
1933	*	*	*	£3.50
1934	*	*	*	£6
1935	*	*	£1.50	£8
1936	*	*	*	£2.50

GEORGE VI

	F	VF	EF	BU
1937	*	*	*	£2.50
1937 proof	*	*	*	£8
1938	*	*	*	£8
1939	*	*	*	£4
1940	*	*	*	£4
1941	*	*	*	£4
1942	*	*	*	£4
1943	*	*	*	£4
1944	*	*	*	£4
1945	*	*	*	£4
1946	*	*	*	£4
1947	*	*	*	£4
1948	*	*	*	£4
1949	*	*	*	£4
1950	*	*	*	£4
1950 proof	*	*	*	£8
1951	*	*	*	£4
1951 proof	*	*	*	£9
1952	*	*	*	£4

ELIZABETH II

	F	VF	EF	BU
1953	*	*	*	£2.50
1954	*	*	*	£2.50
1955	*	*	*	£2.50
1956	*	*	*	£5

■ **FRACTIONS OF FARTHINGS**

Copper Half-Farthings

GEORGE IV	F	VF	EF	BU
1828 Britannia breaks legend	£6	£22	£110	£320
1828 Britannia below legend	£10	£40	£120	£360
1830 trident breaks legend	£8	£28	£110	£310
1830 trident to base of legend	£22	£65	£235	*

	F	VF	EF	BU
WILLIAM IV				
1837	£45	£130	£335	*
VICTORIA				
1839	*	£7	£45	£130
1842	*	£7	£45	£130
1843	*	*	£18	£75
1844	*	*	£18	£75
1844 E/N	£4	£14	£80	£265
1847	*	£7	£22	£90
1851	*	£7	£45	£135
1852	*	£7	£45	£135
1853	*	£9	£50	£150
1853 proof				£700
1854	*	£22	£85	£265
1856	*	£22	£85	£265
1856 large date	£45	£100	£320	*
1868 bronze proof	*			£550
1868 copper-nickel proof	*			£650

Copper Third-Farthings

	F	VF	EF	BU
GEORGE IV				
1827	*	£12	£60	£175
WILLIAM IV				
1835	*	£15	£90	£240
VICTORIA				
1844	*	£25	£85	£325
1844 RE for REG	£25	£60	£325	*

Bronze Third-Farthings

	F	VF	EF	BU
VICTORIA				
1866	*	*	£17	£65
1868	*	*	£17	£65
1876	*	*	£17	£70
1878	*	*	£17	£65
1881	*	*	£17	£70
1884	*	*	£12	£65
1885	*	*	£12	£65
EDWARD VII				
1902	*	*	£9	£30
GEORGE V				
1913	*	*	£9	£30

Copper Quarter-Farthings

	F	VF	EF	BU
VICTORIA				
1839	£9	£17	£35	£135
1851	£9	£17	£45	£135
1852	£9	£17	£45	£135
1853	£9	£20	£55	£135
1853 proof	*	*	*	£650
1868 bronze-proof	*	*	*	£500
1868 copper-nickel proof	*	*	*	£650

MAUNDY SETS

These sets are given out by the monarch each year on Maundy Thursday, the day before Good Friday.
The number of recipients and the amount they receive matches the sovereign's age that year. Maundy coins are newly minted every year, and are legal tender. The first recorded occasion when the sovereign distributed alms at a Maundy service was in 1210, when King John did so at Knaresborough. Extremely Fine prices are for evenly matched sets.

CHARLES II	F	VF	EF
Undated	£210	£3235	£775
1670	£210	£360	£735
1671	£200	£335	£710
1672	£185	£310	£660
1673	£200	£335	£610
1674	£180	£300	£635
1675	£180	£300	£635
1676	£190	£330	£660
1677	£195	£310	£660
1678	£255	£400	£830
1679	£200	£330	£680
1680	£175	£310	£660
1681	£200	£360	£660
1682	£195	£330	£610
1683	£195	£330	£660
1684	£225	£395	£760

JAMES II			
1686	£200	£400	£820
1687	£200	£400	£820
1688	£200	£400	£820

WILLIAM AND MARY			
1689	£535	£1100	*
1691	£390	£720	£1550
1692	£375	£625	£1450
1693	£380	£630	£1550
1694	£360	£585	£1150

WILLIAM III			
1698	£210	£410	£820
1699	£470	£720	£1550
1700	£210	£410	£870
1701	£200	£390	£780

ANNE			
1703	£200	£360	£710
1705	£200	£360	£660
1706	£190	£340	£650
1708	£310	£660	*
1709	£330	£390	£870
1710	£240	£390	£820
1713	£300	£360	£690

GEORGE I			
1723	£200	£310	£700
1727	£190	£330	£720

GEORGE II	F	VF	EF
1729	£160	£255	£520
1731	£160	£255	£520
1732	£160	£255	£520
1735	£160	£255	£520
1737	£160	£255	£520
1739	£160	£255	£520
1740	£160	£255	£520
1743	£180	£280	£585
1746	£160	£250	£490
1760	£160	£250	£440

GEORGE III	F	VF	EF
1763	*	£230	£420
1763 proof		*	£16000
1766	*	£230	£420
1772	*	£240	£435
1780	*	£260	£460
1784	*	£230	£420
1786	*	£235	£420
1792 wire type	*	£325	£575
1795	*	£190	£315
1800	*	£190	£315

	F	VF	EF	Unc
1817	*	£125	£250	£420
1818	*	£125	£250	£420
1820	*	£125	£250	£420

ABOVE: George III Maundy set, 1818

GEORGE IV	F	VF	EF	Unc
1822	*	*	£230	£365
1823	*	*	£230	£365
1824	*	*	£230	£365
1825	*	*	£230	£365
1826	*	*	£230	£365
1827	*	*	£230	£365
1828	*	*	£230	£365
1829	*	*	£230	£365
1830	*	*	£230	£365

WILLIAM IV	F	VF	EF	Unc
1831	*	*	£230	£410
1831 proof	*	*	*	£1650
1831 gold proof	*	*	*	£39000
1832	*	*	£230	£420
1833	*	*	£230	£420

MAUNDY SETS

	F	VF	EF	Unc
1834	*	*	£230	£420
1835	*	*	£230	£420
1836	*	*	£230	£420
1837	*	*	£260	£440

VICTORIA

			EF	Unc
1838			£225	£465
1838 proof			*	£2700
1838 gold proof			*	£29000
1839			£260	£435
1839 proof			£650	£1650
1840			£270	£420
1841			£260	£575
1842			£250	£550
1843			£230	£420
1844			£235	£470
1845			£210	£420
1846			£380	£690
1847			£520	£840
1848			£495	£740
1849			£290	£485
1850			£210	£410
1851			£230	£420
1852			£525	£840
1853			£525	£1000
1853 proof			*	£2400
1854			£220	£385
1855			£220	£340
1856			£190	£410
1857			£210	£340
1858			£190	£340
1859			£190	£340
1860			£190	£340
1861			£190	£340
1862			£210	£360
1863			£230	£420
1864			£190	£340
1865			£190	£340
1866			£190	£340
1867			£190	£340
1868			£190	£340
1869			£235	£380
1870			£180	£290
1871			£170	£290
1872			£170	£290
1873			£170	£290
1874			£170	£290
1875			£170	£290
1876			£170	£290
1877			£170	£290
1878			£170	£290
1879			£170	£290
1880			£170	£290
1881			£160	£290
1882			£160	£290
1883			£160	£290
1884			£160	£290
1885			£160	£290
1886			£160	£290
1887			£160	£225
1888 JH			£150	£225
1889			£150	£225
1890			£150	£225
1891			£150	£225
1892			£150	£225
1893 OH			£150	£175
1894			£130	£195
1895			£120	£175
1896			£120	£175
1897			£120	£175
1898			£120	£175
1899			£120	£175
1900			£120	£175
1901			£120	£175

EDWARD VII

			EF	Unc
1902			£110	£170
1902 matt proof			*	£270
1903–08			£110	£145
1909–10			£175	£265

GEORGE V

			EF	Unc
1911			£145	£290
1911 proof			*	£270
1912–36			£145	£240

GEORGE VI

			EF	Unc
1937			£125	£210
1938–52			£145	£240

ELIZABETH II

			EF	Unc
1953			*	£1100
1953 proof gold				ext. rare
1953 matt proof				ext. rare
1954–69			*	£200
1970–99			*	£210
2000			*	£210
2001			*	£210
2002			*	£210
2002 gold from set			*	£2200
2003			*	£210
2004			*	£210
2005			*	£210
2006			*	£210
2007			*	£240
2008			*	£575
2009			*	£500
2010			*	£495
2011			*	£495
2012			*	£495
2013			*	£475
2014			*	£600
2015			*	£625
2016			*	£625
2017			*	£620
2018			*	£700
2019			*	£750
2020			*	£725
2021			*	£775

DECIMAL COINAGE

■ BRITANNIAS

A United Kingdom gold bullion coin, introduced in the autumn of 1987, which contains one ounce of 22ct gold and has a face value of £100. There are also ½ ounce, ¼ ounce and 1/10 ounce versions, with face values of £50, £25 and £10 respectively. The ½ and ¼ oz are issued only in sets. All are legal tender.

The coins bear a portrait of the Queen on the obverse and the figure of Britannia on the reverse.

BV means bullion value. At the time of going to press gold is around £1000 per troy ounce and platinum is around £1100 per troy ounce.

1987–2005 1oz, proof	*
1987–2005 1/10 oz, proof	*
1987–2005 ½ oz, proof	*
1987–2005 ¼ oz, proof	*

To commemorate the 10th anniversary of the first Britannia issue, new reverse designs were introduced for the gold coins. A series of four silver coins with denominations from £2 to 20 pence was also issued. The silver coins were issued only in proof condition in 1997.

1997 1oz, ¼oz and 1/10oz issued individually; all coins issued in 4-coin sets
1997 1oz, ¼ oz silver coins issued individually; all coins issued in 4-coin sets
1998 gold and silver coins issued with new portrait of HM the Queen and first reverse design
2001 new reverse designs introduced
For all issues from 2011 see the Royal Mint website.

■ FIVE POUNDS

Crown sized.

1990 Queen Mother's 90th birthday, gold, proof	BV
1990 silver, proof	£32
1990 cu–ni, BU	£6.50
1990 cu–ni, specimen	£9
1993 40th Anniversary of the Coronation, gold, proof	BV
1993 silver, proof	£32
1993 cu–ni, specimen	£9
1993 cu–ni, BU	£7.50
1993 cu–ni, proof, originally issued in a Royal Mint set	£7.50
1996 Queen's 70th Birthday, gold, proof	BV
1996 silver, proof	£32
1996 cu–ni, BU	£7.50
1996 cu–ni, proof, originally issued in a Royal Mint set	£7.50
1996 cu–ni, specimen	£9
1997 Golden Wedding, gold, proof	BV
1997 silver, proof	£32
1997 cu–ni, BU	£7.50
1997 cu–ni, proof, originally issued in a Royal Mint set	£7.50
1997 cu–ni, specimen	£10
1998 Prince Charles 50th Birthday, gold, proof	BV
1998 silver, proof	£65
1998 cu–ni, BU	£7.50
1998 cu–ni, proof, originally issued in a Royal Mint set	£11
1998 cu–ni, specimen	£9
1999 Diana Memorial, gold, proof	BV
1999 silver, proof	£42
1999 cu–ni, proof, originally issued in a Royal Mint set	£11
1999 cu–ni, BU	£7.50
1999 cu–ni, specimen	£9
1999 Millennium, gold, proof	BV
1999 silver, proof	£42
1999 cu–ni, BU	£6.50
1999 cu–ni, specimen	£9
2000 gold, proof	BV
2000 silver with 22 carat gold, proof	£42
2000 cu–ni, BU	£6.50
2000 cu–ni, specimen	£14
2000 cu–ni, proof, originally issued in a Royal Mint set	£13
2000 cu–ni, specimen, Dome mintmark	£16
2000 silver, proof	£60
2000 Queen Mother commemorative, gold, proof	BV
2000 silver, proof	£42
2000 silver piedfort	£60
2000 cu–ni, BU	£6.50
2000 cu–ni, proof, originally issued in a Royal Mint set	£7.50
2001 Victorian Era anniversary, gold, proof	BV
2001 gold, proof with reverse frosting	BV
2001 silver, proof	£48
2001 silver, proof with reverse frosting	£95
2001 cu–ni, BU	£6.50
2001 cu–ni, proof, originally issued in a Royal Mint set	£11
2001 cu–ni, specimen	£9
2002 Golden Jubilee, gold proof	BV
2002 silver, proof	£55
2002 cu–ni, BU	£5.50
2002 cu–ni, proof, originally issued in a Royal Mint set	£9.50
2002 cu–ni, specimen	£8.50
2002 Queen Mother memorial, gold, proof	BV
2002 silver, proof	£38
2002 cu–ni, BU	£7.50
2002 cu–ni proof, originally issued in a Royal Mint set	£13
2003 Coronation commemorative, gold proof	BV
2003 silver, proof	£38
2003 cu–ni, BU	£6.50
2003 cu–ni, proof, originally issued in a Royal Mint set	£9
2003 cu–ni, specimen	£9.50
2004 Entente Cordiale, gold, proof	BV
2004 platinum, piedfort, proof	BV
2004 silver piedfort, proof	£105
2004 silver, proof	£50
2004 Entente Cordiale, cu–ni, proof	£16
2004 specimen	£11
2004 BU	£5.50
2005 Trafalgar, gold, proof	BV
2005 silver piedfort, proof	£120
2005 silver, proof	£42
2005 cu–ni, proof, originally issued in a Royal Mint set	£9
2005 specimen	£9
2005 BU	£5.50
2005 Nelson, gold, proof	BV
2005 platinum, piedfort, proof	BV
2005 silver piedfort, proof	£120
2005 silver, proof	£50
1998 cu–ni, specimen	£9

2005 cu–ni, proof, originally issued in a Royal Mint set	£9
2005 BU	£5.50
2005 specimen	£9
2006 Queen's 80th Birthday, gold, proof	BV
2006 platinum, piedfort, proof	BV
2006 silver piedfort, proof	£70
2006 silver, proof	£38
2006 cu–ni, proof, originally issued in a Royal Mint set	£9
2006 specimen	£9
2006 BU	£5.50
2007 Diamond Wedding, gold, proof	BV
2007 silver piedfort, proof	£100
2007 silver, proof	£48
2007 cu–ni, proof, originally issued in a Royal Mint set	£14
2008 Elizabeth I, platinum, piedfort, proof	BV
2008 gold, proof	BV
2008 silver piedfort, proof	£90
2008 silver, proof	£48
2008 BU	£5.50
2009 Henry VIII, gold, proof	BV
2009 silver piedfort, proof	£84
2009 silver, proof	£48
2009 Countdown to London gold proof	BV
2009 silver piedfort, proof	£95
2010 Restoration of Monarchy gold proof	BV
2010 silver piedfort, proof	£42
2010 Countdown to London silver, piedforf, proof	£105
2010 silver, proof	£42
2010 BU	£5.50

◼ TWO POUNDS

1986 Commonwealth Games, proof gold	BV
1986 silver, proof	£22
1986 silver unc	£17
1986 proof, nickel brass, originally issued in a Royal Mint set	£5.50
1986 specimen	£4.50
1986 unc	£3.50
1989 Bill of Rights, silver piedfort, proof, originally issued in a Royal Mint set	£65
1989 silver, proof	£38
1989 proof, nickel brass, originally issued in a Royal Mint set	£7.50
1989 specimen	£4.50
1989 unc	£3.50
1989 Claim of Rights, silver piedfort proof, originally issued in a Royal Mint set	£63
1989 silver, proof	£38
1989 proof, nickel brass, originally issued in a Royal Mint set	£7.60
1989 specimen	£4.50
1989 unc	£3.50
1994 Bank of England, gold, proof	BV
1994 gold 'mule', proof	BV
1994 silver piedfort, proof	£42
1994 silver, proof	£32
1994 proof, nickel brass, originally issued in a Royal Mint set	£5.50
1994 specimen	£4.50
1994 in folder, BU	£3.50
1995 50th Anniversary of end of	

Second World War, gold, proof	BV
1995 silver piedfort, proof	£42
1995 silver, proof	£33
1995 proof, nickel brass, originally issued in a Royal Mint set	£5.50
1995 specimen	£4.50
1995 BU	£3.50
1995 50th Anniversary of United Nations, gold, proof	BV
1995 silver piedfort, proof	£42
1995 silver, proof	£32
1995 specimen	£4.50
1995 BU	£3.50
1996 European Football, gold, proof	BV
1996 silver piedfort, proof	£43
1996 silver, proof	£32
1996 proof, nickel brass, originally issued in a Royal Mint set	£5.50
1996 specimen	£4.50
1996 BU	£3.50
1997 Iron Age, bimetal, gold, proof	BV
1997 silver piedfort, proof	£42
1997 silver, proof	£32
1997 proof, originally issued in a Royal Mint set	£5.50
1997 specimen	£4.50
1997 BU	£3.50
1997 Britannia chariot, proof, 1 oz fine silver	£38
1998 bimetal, silver, proof	£32
1998 silver piedfort	£63
1998 proof, originally issued in a Royal Mint set	£6.50
1998 in folder, BU	£6.50
1998 Britannia standing, proof, 1 oz fine silver	£28
1998 unc	£11
1999 Rugby World Cup, gold, proof	BV
1999 silver piedfort, proof	£75
1999 silver, proof	£38
1999 proof, originally issued in a Royal Mint set	£5.50
1999 BU	£3.50
2000 bimetal, silver, proof, originally issued in a Royal Mint set	£32
2000 proof, originally issued in a Royal Mint set	£5.50
2000 Britannia standing, unc, 1 oz fine silver	£28
2001 Marconi commemorative, gold, proof	BV
2001 silver piedfort, proof	£73
2001 silver, proof	£38
2001 with reverse frosting, silver, proof	£42
2001 proof, originally issued in a Royal Mint set	£7.50
2001 specimen	£5.50
2001 BU	£3.50
2002 Iron Age, gold proof	BV
2002 Commonwealth Games, gold, proof, four different reverses	*
2002 Commonwealth Games, silver, proof, four different reverses	*
2002 Commonwealth Games, piedfort, four different reverses	*
2002 Commonwealth Games, BU, four different reverses	*
2002 Britannia standing, unc, 1 oz fine silver	£11
2003 DNA gold bi-metal proof	BV
2003 silver piedfort, proof	£75
2003 silver, proof	£38

2003 specimen	£5.50
2003 proof, originally issued in a Royal Mint set	£6.50
2003 BU	£3.50
2003 Britannia helmeted, silver, proof	£38
2003 silver	£14
2004 Locomotive, gold, proof	BV
2004 silver piedfort, proof	£65
2004 silver, proof	£37
2004 BU, silver	£24
2004 proof, originally issued in a Royal Mail set	£6.60
2004 specimen	£6.50
2004 BU	£3.50
2004 Britannia standing, proof, 1 oz fine silver	£27
2004 unc	£24
2005 400th Gunpowder Plot gold, proof	BV
2005 silver piedfort, proof	£75
2005 silver, proof	£33
2005 proof, originally issued in a Royal Mint set	£6.50
2005 specimen	£5.50
2005 BU	£3.50
2005 World War II, gold proof	BV
2005 silver, proof, piedfort	£75
2005 silver, proof	£32
2005 specimen	£5.50
2005 BU	£3.50
2005 Britannia seated, silver, proof	£32
2005 silver, unc	£15
2006 Brunel the Man, gold, proof	BV
2006 silver, proof, piedfort	£84
2006 silver, proof	£33
2006 proof, originally issued in a Royal Mint set	£7.50
2006 specimen	£9
2006 BU	£3.50
2006 Britannia seated, silver, proof	£38
2007 Abolition of the Slave Trade, gold, proof	BV
2007 silver, proof	£38
2007 Act of Union, silver, proof	£38
2007 Britannia, silver	£24
2007 BU	£3.50
2008 Olympiad London, gold, proof	BV
2008 silver, proof, piedfort	£75
2008 silver, proof	£32
2008 specimen	£8.50
2008 BU	£3.50
2009 Brunel, gold, proof	BV
2009 Paddington London, gold, proof	BV
2009 Brunel, piedfort, silver proof	£80
2009 Darwin, piedfort silver proof	£75
2009 silver, proof	£42
2009 Burns, silver proof	£38
2009 Darwin, silver proof	£38
2009 BU	face
2009 Burns, cu–ni, BU	£3.50
2009 Darwin, cu–ni, BU	£3.50
2010 Nightingale, gold proof	BV
2010 silver, proof	£42
2010 Nightingale, silver proof	£38
2010 Nightingale, piedfort silver proof	£75

2010 BU	face
2010 Nightingale, cu–ni, BU	face

■ ONE POUND

1983	£3.50
1983 specimen	£4.50
1983 proof, originally issued in a Royal Mint set	£4.50
1983 silver, proof	£22
1983 silver, proof, piedfort	£55
1984 Scottish reverse	£3.50
1984 specimen	£4.50
1984 proof, originally issued in a Royal Mint set	£4.50
1984 silver, proof	£22
1984 silver, proof, piedfort	£48
1985 new portrait, Welsh reverse	£4.50
1985 specimen	£4.50
1985 proof, originally issued in a Royal Mint set	£4.50
1985 silver, proof	£22
1985 silver, proof, piedfort	£48
1986 Northern Ireland reverse	£5.50
1986 specimen	£4.50
1986 proof, originally issued in a Royal Mint set	£4.50
1986 silver, proof	£22
1986 silver, proof, piedfort	£4.50
1987 English reverse	£4.50
1987 specimen	£4.50
1987 proof, originally issued in a Royal Mint set	£4.50
1987 silver, proof	£22
1987 silver, proof, piedfort	£48
1988 Royal coat of arms reverse	£5.50
1988 specimen	£4.50
1988 proof, originally issued in a Royal Mint set	£4.50
1988 silver, proof	£28
1988 silver, proof, piedfort	£42
1989 Scottish reverse as 1984	£4.50
1989 proof, originally issued in a Royal Mint set	£4.50
1989 silver, proof	£22
1990 Welsh reverse as 1985	£5.50
1990 proof, originally issued in a Royal Mint set	£4.50
1990 silver, proof	£22
1991 Northern Ireland reverse as 1986	£4.50
1991 proof, originally issued in a Royal Mint set	£4.50
1991 silver, proof	£22
1992 English reverse as 1987	£4.50
1992 proof, originally issued in a Royal Mint set	£4.50
1992 silver, proof	£22
1993 Royal coat of arms reverse as 1983	£38
1993 proof, originally issued in a Royal Mint set	£4.50
1993 silver, proof	£22
1993 silver, proof, piedfort	£38
1994 Scottish Lion	£4.50
1994 specimen	£4.50
1994 proof, originally issued in a Royal Mint set	£5.50
1994 silver, proof	£22
1994 silver, proof, piedfort	£42
1995 Welsh dragon	£4.50
1995 specimen, English version	£4.50
1995 specimen, Welsh version	£7.50
1995 proof, originally issued in a Royal Mint set	£5.50
1995 silver, proof	£22

1995 silver, proof, piedfort	£75
1996 Northern Ireland Celtic Ring	£4.50
1996 specimen	£4.50
1996 proof, originally issued in a Royal Mint set	£5.50
1995 silver, proof	£22
1995 silver, proof, piedfort	£55
1997 English Lions	£5.50
1997 specimen	£4.50
1997 proof, originally issued in a Royal Mint set	£5.50
1997 silver, proof	£22
1997 silver, proof, piedfort	£55
1998 Royal coat of arms reverse as 1983	£4.50
1998 proof, originally issued in a Royal Mint set	£5.50
1998 silver, proof	£22
1998 silver, proof, piedfort	£42
1999 Scottish Lion reverse as 1984	£3.50
1999 specimen	£4.50
1999 proof, originally issued in a Royal Mint set	£4.50
1999 silver, proof	£22
1999 with reverse frosting	£22
1999 silver, proof, piedfort	£38
2000 Welsh Dragon reverse as 1995	£3.50
2000 proof, originally issued in a Royal Mint set	£5.50
2000 silver, proof	£22
2000 silver, proof, with reverse frosting	£22
2000 silver, proof, piedfort	£33
2001 Northern Ireland reverse as 1996	£4.50
2001 proof, originally issued in a Royal Mint set	£5.50
2001 silver, proof	£22
2001 silver, proof, with reverse frosting	£38
2001 silver, proof, piedfort	£38
2002 English design, reverse as 1997	£4.50
2002 gold proof, originally issued in a Royal Mint set	BV
2002 proof, originally issued in a Royal Mint set	£5.50
2002 silver, proof	£22
2002 silver, proof, with reverse frosting	£22
2002 silver, proof, piedfort	£38
2003 Royal Arms	£4.50
2003 proof, originally issued in a Royal Mint set	£9
2003 silver, proof	£22
2003 silver, proof, piedfort	£38
2003 Forth Rail Bridge, 'pattern', silver, proof, originally issued in a Royal Mint set	*
2004 Dragon, 'pattern', silver, proof, originally issued in a Royal Mint set	*
2005 gold proof, originally issued in a Royal Mint set	BV
2004 Unicorn, 'pattern', silver, proof, originally issued in a Royal Mint set	*
2004 Stag, 'pattern', silver, proof, originally issued in a Royal Mint set	*
2004 Lion, 'pattern', silver, proof, originally issued in a Royal Mint set	*
2004 Forth Rail Bridge	£3.50
2004 specimen	£5.50
2004 proof, originally issued in a Royal Mint set	£9
2004 silver, proof	£22
2004 silver, proof, piedfort	£38
2004 gold, proof	BV
2005 Menai Bridge	£4.50
2005 specimen	£5.50

2005 proof, originally issued in a Royal Mint set	£9
2005 silver, proof	£22
2005 silver, proof, piedfort	£38
2005 gold, proof	BV
2006 Egyptian Arch	£4.50
2006 specimen	£5.50
2006 proof, originally issued in a Royal Mint set	£9
2006 silver, proof	£22
2006 silver, proof, piedfort	£38
2006 gold, proof	BV
2007 Millennium Bridge, gold proof	BV
2007 silver, proof, piedfort	£38
2007 silver, proof	£22
2007 proof	£11
2007 BU	£4.50
2008 Forth, Menai, Egyptian Arch and Millennium Bridges, gold proof, originally issued in a Royal Mint set	BV
2008 Royal Arms, gold, proof	BV
2008 silver, proof, piedfort	£38
2008 silver, proof	£22
2008 proof	£7.50
2008 BU	£4.50
2009 Royal Arms, gold, proof	BV
2009 silver, proof, piedfort	£38
2009 silver, proof	£22
2009 proof	£6.50
2009 BU	£5.50
2010 Royal Arms, gold, proof	BV
2010 silver, proof, piedfort	£38
2010 silver, proof	£22
2010 proof	£6.50
2010 BU	£4.50
2010 London, gold, proof	BV
2010 silver, proof, piedfort	£38
2010 silver, proof	£22
2010 proof	£6.50
2010 BU	£4.50
2010 Belfast, gold, proof	BV
2010 silver, proof, piedfort	£38
2010 silver, proof	£22
2010 proof	£6.50
2010 BU	£3.50

Note: edge inscriptions on £2 and £1 are either upright or inverted in relation to the obverse.

■ FIFTY PENCE

1969 unc	£2.25
1970 unc	£3.25
1971 proof, originally issued in a Royal Mint set	£3.35
1972 proof, originally issued in a Royal Mint set	£4.50
1973 EEC proof, originally issued in a Royal Mint set	£3.35
1973 EEC proof, VIP	ext. rare
1973 unc	£1.25
1974 proof, originally issued in a Royal Mint set	£3.50
1975 proof, originally issued in a Royal Mint set	£3.50
1976 proof, originally issued in a Royal Mint set	£2.50
1976 unc	£1.25
1977 proof, originally issued in a Royal Mint set	£2.50
1977 unc	£1.25
1978 proof	£2.50

1978 unc	£1.25
1979 proof, originally issued in a Royal Mint set	£2.50
1979 unc	£1.25
1980 proof, originally issued in a Royal Mint set	£2.50
1980 unc	£1.25
1981 proof, originally issued in a Royal Mint set	£2.50
1981 unc	£1.25
1982 proof, originally issued in a Royal Mint set	£2.50
1982 unc	£1.25
1983 proof, originally issued in a Royal Mint set	£2.50
1983 unc	£1.25
1984 proof, originally issued in a Royal Mint set	£2.50
1984 unc	£3.50
1985 proof, originally issued in a Royal Mint set	£2.50
1985 unc	£4.50
1986 proof, originally issued in a Royal Mint set	£2.50
1986 unc	£2.50
1987 proof, originally issued in a Royal Mint set	£3.50
1987 unc	£2.50
1988 proof, originally issued in a Royal Mint set	£3.50
1988 unc	£2.50
1989 proof, originally issued in a Royal Mint set	£2.50
1989 unc	£3.50
1990 proof, originally issued in a Royal Mint set	£4.50
1990 unc	£3.50
1991 proof, originally issued in a Royal Mint set	£4.50
1991 unc	£2.50
1992 proof	£4.50
1992 unc	£2.50
1992 European Community	£5.50
1992 specimen	£2.50
1992 proof, originally issued in a Royal Mint set	£7.50
1992 silver, proof	£22
1992 silver, proof, piedfort	£38
1992 gold, proof	BV
1993 proof	£3.50
1993 unc	£3.50
1994 Normandy Landings	£2.50
1994 specimen	£2.50
1994 proof, originally issued in a Royal Mint set	£4.50
1994 silver, proof	£27
1994 silver, proof, piedfort	£50
1994 gold, proof	£730
1995 proof	£3.50
1995 unc	£2.50
1996 proof	£3.50
1996 unc	£2.50
1996 silver, proof	£17
1997 unc	£2.50
1997 proof	£3.50
1997 silver, proof	£2.50
1997 new size (27.3mm diameter), unc	£2.50
1997 proof, originally issued in a Royal Mint set	£4.50
1997 silver, proof	£20
1997 silver, proof, piedfort	£38
1998 proof, originally issued in a Royal Mint set	£2.50
1998 unc	£1.25
1998 European Presidency	£2.50
1998 specimen	£2.50
1998 silver, proof	£22
1998 silver, proof, piedfort	£38
1998 gold, proof	£730
1998 NHS, unc	£2.50
1998 proof, originally issued in a Royal Mint set	£2.50
1999 silver, proof	£27
1999 silver piedfort	£38
1999 gold, proof	£730
1999 proof, originally issued in a Royal Mint set	£2.50
1999 unc	face
2000 proof, originally issued in a Royal Mint set	£2.50
2000 unc	face
2000 silver, proof	£17
2000 Library Commemorative, unc	£2.50
2000 specimen	£5.50
2000 proof, originally issued in a Royal Mint set	£2.50
2000 silver, proof	£27
2000 silver, proof, piedfort	£38
2000 gold, proof	£730
2002 gold proof, originally issued in a Royal Mint set	£730
2003 Suffragette, unc	£1.25
2003 proof, originally issued in a Royal Mint set	£4.50
2003 specimen	£3.50
2003 silver, proof	£22
2003 silver, proof, piedfort	£38
2003 gold, proof	£730
2004 Roger Bannister, unc	£1.25
2004 specimen	£4.50
2004 proof, originally issued in a Royal Mint set	£4.50
2004 silver, proof	£22
2004 silver, proof piedfort	£28
2005 Samuel Johnson, unc	£1.25
2005 proof, originally issued in a Royal Mint set	£4.50
2005 silver, proof	£4.50
2005 silver, proof, piedfort	£38
2005 gold proof	£700
2006 Victoria Cross, unc	£1.25
2006 proof, originally issued in a Royal Mint set	£4.50
2006 specimen	£3.50
2006 silver, proof	£22
2006 silver, proof, piedfort	£38
2006 gold, proof	£730
2007 Scouting Centenary, gold, proof	£730
2007 silver, proof	£28
2007 silver piedfort, proof	£50
2008 issued in sets only	*
2009 gold, proof	£730
2009 silver, proof	£28
2009 unc	£1.25
2010 England, gold, proof	£730
2010 silver piedfort, proof	£50
2010 silver, proof	£35
2010 Northern Ireland, gold, proof	£730
2010 silver piedfort, proof	£50
2010 silver, proof	£28
2010 Shield, silver proof	£28

■ TWENTY–FIVE PENCE (crown)

1972 Silver Wedding	£1.25
1972 proof, originally issued in a Royal Mint set	£4.50

1972 silver, proof	£22
1977 Jubilee	£1.25
1977 proof, originally issued in a Royal Mint set	£4.50
1977 specimen	£2.50
1977 silver, proof	£22
1980 Queen Mother 80th Birthday	£1.25
1980 specimen	£2.50
1980 silver, proof	£28
1981 Royal Wedding	£1.25
1981 specimen	£3.50
1981 silver, proof	£28

■ TWENTY PENCE

1982–2010 unc	£1.75
1982–2010 BU	£3.50
1982–2010 proof, originally issued in a Royal Mint set	£3.50
1982 silver, proof, piedfort	£30
2000 silver, proof, originally issued in a Royal Mint set	*
2002 gold proof, originally issued in a Royal Mint set	£400
2008, 2008 new rev. gold proofs	£400
2008, 2008 new rev. platinum proofs	£820
2006–2010 silver, proof	£22
2009 error, obverse of 2008, no date	£50

■ TEN PENCE

1968–1981 new pence	from	£1
1972 & 1981 proof, originally issued in a Royal Mint set		£2
1982–1984 pence, unc & proof, originally issued in a Royal Mint set		£2
1985–1992 unc & proof, originally issued in a Royal Mint set		£2.25
1992–1997 new size: 24.5mm diameter, 1993 & 1994 issued in sets only	from	£1
1992–1997 proof, originally issued in a Royal Mint set		£2.25
1992 silver, proof		£11
1992 silver, proof, piedfort		£22
1996 silver, proof		£11
1998–2007, 1998, 1999 & 2007 issued in sets only		face
1998–2010 proof, originally issued in a Royal Mint set		£2.25
2002 gold proof, originally issued in a Royal Mint set		£375
2008 gold proof		£375
2008 new reverse, gold proof		£375
2008 platinum proof		£570
2008 new reverse, platinum proof		£570
2008 new reverse, silver piedfort proof		£33
2006–2010 silver, proof		£17

■ FIVE PENCE

1968–81, 1972–74, 1976 & 1981 issued in sets only	£0.25
1971–1981 proof, originally issued in a Royal Mint set	£1.25
1982–1984 proof, unc, originally issued in a Royal Mint set	£1.25
1985–1990, 1985, 1996 & 1990 issued in sets only	face
1985–1990 proof, originally issued in a Royal Mint set	£2
1990–1997	face
1990–1997 proof, originally issued in a Royal Mint set	£2.25
1990 silver, proof, originally issued in a Royal Mint set	£11

1990 silver, proof piedfort	£22
1996 silver, proof	£11
1998–2008, 2007–8 issued in sets only	face
1998–2010 proof, originally issued in a Royal Mint set	£3.25
2000 silver, proof	*
2002 gold proof, originally issued in a Royal Mint set	£320
2008 gold proof	£240
2008 new reverse, gold proof	£240
2008 platinum proof	£300
2008 new reverse, platinum proof	£300
2008 new reverse, silver piedfort proof	£22
2006–2010 silver, proof	£15

■ TWO PENCE

11971–1981, 1972 & 1974 issued in sets only	face
1971–1981 proof, originally issued in a Royal Mint set	£1.25
1982–1984 new reverse	face
1983, mule, old reverse issued in sets	£410
1982–1984 proof, originally issued in a Royal Mint set	£1.25
1985–1992 1992 issued in sets only	face
1985–1992 proof, originally issued in a Royal Mint set	£1.25
1992–1997	face
1993–1997 proof, originally issued in a Royal Mint set	£1.25
1996, 2000, 2006, 2008 silver proof	£14
2002 gold proof, originally issued in a Royal Mint set	£480
1998–2010	face
1998–2010 proof originally issued in a Royal Mint set	£1.25
2008 gold proof	£475
2008 new reverse, gold proof	£475
2008 platinum proof	£550
2008 new reverse, platinum proof	£550
2008 new reverse, silver piedfort proof	£33
2006–2010 silver proof	£13

■ ONE PENNY

1971–1981, 1972 issued in sets only	from	£1
1971–1981 proof, originally issued in a Royal Mint set		£1.25
1982–1984 new reverse, proof, unc, originally issued in a Royal Mint set		£1.25
1985–1992, 1992 issued in sets only		face
1985–1992 proof, originally issued in a Royal Mint set		£1.25
1992–1997		face
1993–1997 proof, originally issued in a Royal Mint set		£1.25
1996 silver, proof, originally issued in a Royal Mint set		£13
2002 gold proof, originally issued in a Royal Mint set		£240
2008 gold proof		£240
2008 new reverse, gold proof		£240
2008 platinum proof		£290
2008 new reverse, platinum proof		£290
2008 new reverse, silver piedfort proof		£22
1998–2010		face
1998–2010 proof, originally issued in a Royal Mint set		£1.25

■ HALF PENNY

1971–1981	£0.10
1971–1981 proof, originally issued in a Royal Mint set	£1.25
1982–1984 new reverse	face
1982–1984 proof, originally issued in a Royal Mint set	£1.25

PROOF & SPECIMEN SETS

Proof or specimen sets have been issued since 1887 by the Royal Mint. Before then sets were issued privately by the engraver.

Some sets are of currency coins, easily distinguishable from proofs, which have a vastly superior finish. The two 1887 sets frequently come on to the market, hence their place in this list.

The 1953 'plastic' set, though made up of currency coins, is official and was issued in a plastic packet, hence the name. Sets are proof sets unless stated.

	FDC
GEORGE IV	
1826 new issue, £5–farthing (11 coins) from	£140000
WILLIAM IV	
1831 Coronation, £2–farthing (14 coins) from	£85000
VICTORIA	
1839 young head, 'Una and the Lion'	
£5, sovereign–farthing (15 coins) from	£385000
1853 sovereign–half farthing,	
inc Gothic crown (16 coins) from	£110000
1887 Jubilee head, £5–threepence	
('full set': 11 coins) from	£45000
1887 currency set, unofficial	£5250
1887 crown–threepence ('short set': 7 coins)	£4750
1887 currency set, unofficial	£750
1893 old head, £5–threepence	
('full set': 10 coins) from	£50000
1893 crown–threepence ('short set': 6 coins)	£7750
EDWARD VII	
1902 Coronation, £5–Maundy penny,	
matt proofs (13 coins)	£6750
1902 sovereign–Maundy penny, matt proofs (11 coins)	£2400
GEORGE V	
1911 Coronation, £5–Maundy penny (12 coins)	£19000
1911 sovereign–Maundy penny (10 coins)	£3750
1911 halfcrown–Maundy penny (8 coins)	£1600
1927 new types, crown–threepence (6 coins)	£850
GEORGE VI	
1937 Coronation, gold set, £5–half sovereign (4 coins)	£13500
1937 silver and bronze set, crown–farthing	
including Maundy money (15 coins)	£475
1950 mid-century, halfcrown–farthing (9 coins)	£160
1951 Festival of Britain, crown–farthing (10 coins)	£220
ELIZABETH II	
1953 Coronation, crown–farthing (10 coins)	£110
1953 currency, official, known as the 'plastic' set,	
halfcrown–farthing (9 coins)	£22
Specimen decimal set, 1968 10p, 5p;	
1971 2p, 1p, ½p in blue wallet (5 coins)	£1.50
1970 last £sd coins, (issued 1971-73),	
halfcrown–halfpenny (8 coins)	£19

1971 decimal (issued 1973),	
50p, 10p, 5p, 2p, 1p, ½p (6 coins)	£13
1972 decimal 50p, Silver Wedding	
25p, 10p, 5p, 2p, 1p, ½p (7 coins)	£18
1973-76 decimal, 50p–½p (6 coins)	£14
1977 decimal 50p–½p and Jubilee crown (7 coins)	£14
1978 decimal, 50p–½p (6 coins)	£14
1979 decimal, 50p–½p (6 coins)	£14
1980 decimal, 50p–½p (6 coins)	£14
1980 gold, £5, £2, sovereign, half sovereign (4 coins)	BV
1981 commemorative, £5, sovereign,	
Royal Wedding silver crown, 50p–½p (9 coins)	£2250
1981 commemorative, sovereign and	
Royal Wedding silver crown (2 coins)	£380
1981 decimal, 50p–½p (6 coins)	£14
1982 gold, £5, £2, sovereign, half sovereign (4 coins	BV
1982 decimal, 50p–½p including 20p (7 coins)	£14
1982 uncirculated decimal,	
50p–½p including 20p (7 coins)	£7
1983 gold, £2, sovereign, half sovereign (3 coins)	BV
1983 decimal, £1–½p (8 coins)	£16
1983 uncirculated decimal, £1–½ p (8 coins)	£14
1984 gold, £5, sovereign, half sovereign (3 coins)	BV
1984 decimal, £1 Scottish rev–½p (8 coins)	£17
1984 uncirculated decimal, £1	
Scottish rev–½p (8 coins)	£11
1985 gold, new portrait, £5, £2,	
sovereign, half sovereign (4 coins)	BV
1985 decimal, £1 Welsh	
rev–1p (7 coins) in deluxe case	£22
1985 in standard case	£13
1985 uncirculated decimal, £1 Welsh rev–1p (7 coins)£11	
1986 gold, Commonwealth Games,	
£2, sovereign, half sovereign (3 coins)	BV
1986 decimal, Commonwealth Games £2,	
Northern Ireland £1–1p	
(8 coins) in deluxe case	£27
1986 in standard case	£20
1986 uncirculated decimal, in folder	£11
1987 gold Britannia, £100–£10 (4 coins)	BV
1987 decimal, £25, £10 (2 coins)	BV
1987 gold, £2, sovereign, half sovereign (3 coins)	BV
1987 decimal, £1 English rev–1p (7 coins) in deluxe case	£27
1987 in standard case	£18
1987 uncirculated decimal, in folder	£9
1988 gold Britannia, £100–£10 (4 coins)	BV
1988 £25, £10 (2 coins)	BV
1988 £2, sovereign, half sovereign (3 coins)	BV
1988 £1 Royal Arms rev–1p (7 coins) in deluxe case	£25
1988 in standard case	£15
1988 uncirculated decimal, in folder	£10
1989 gold Britannia, £100–£10 (4 coins)	BV
1989 £25, £10 (2 coins)	BV
1989 gold 500th anniversary of the sovereign,	
£5, £2, sovereign, half sovereign (4 coins)	£5300
1989 gold 500th anniversary of the sovereign,	
£2, sovereign, half sovereign (2 coins)	£2700
1989 decimal, Bill of Rights £2, Claim of Right	
£2, £1 Scottish rev, 50p–1p (9 coins) in deluxe case	£37
1989 in standard case	£25

1989 silver, Bill of Rights £2, Claim of Right £2 (2 coins)	£55
1989 silver piedfort, £2 as above (2 coins)	£85
1989 uncirculated, decimal, £2, in folder (2 coins)	£13
1989 uncirculated decimal, in folder, £1 Scottish rev–1p (7 coins)	£20
1990 gold Britannia, £100–£10 (4 coins)	BV
1990 gold, £5, £2, sovereign, half sovereign (4 coins)	BV
1990 £2, sovereign, half sovereign (3 coins)	BV
1990 silver, 5p, large and small size (2 coins)	£30
1990 decimal, £1 Welsh rev–1p including large and small 5p (8 coins) in deluxe case	£32
1990 in standard case	£22
1990 uncirculated decimal, in folder, £1 Welsh rev as 1985–1p including large and small 5p (8 coins)	£19
1991 gold Britannia, £100–£10 (4 coins)	BV
1991 gold, £5, £2, sovereign, half sovereign (4 coins)	BV
1991 £2, sovereign, half sovereign (3 coins)	BV
1991 decimal, £1–1p (7 coins) in deluxe case	£36
1991 in standard case	£27
1991 uncirculated decimal, in folder,	£18
1992 gold Britannia, £100–£10 (4 coins)	BV
1992 gold, £5, £2, sovereign, half sovereign (4 coins)	BV
1992 £2, sovereign, half sovereign (3 coins)	BV
1992 silver, ten pence, large and small size (2 coins)	£33
1992 decimal, £1 English rev–1p including two 50p, new 10p (9 coins) in deluxe case	£33
1992 in standard case	£28
1992 uncirculated decimal, in folder	£19
1993 gold Britannia, £100–£10 (4 coins)	BV
1993 gold, £5, £2, sovereign, half sovereign (4 coins)	BV
1993 £2, sovereign, half sovereign (3 coins)	BV
1993 Coronation Anniversary £5, £1–1p (8 coins), in deluxe case	£40
1993 in standard case	£33
1993 uncirculated decimal, with two 50p, no £5 (8 coins)	£22
1994 gold Britannia, £100–£10 (4 coins)	BV
1994 gold, Bank of England, £5, £2 sovereign, half sovereign (4 coins)	BV
1994 £2 Bank of England, sovereign, half sovereign (3 coins)	BV
1994 decimal, £2 Bank of England, £1 Scottish rev, 50p D Day–1p (8 coins) in deluxe case	£36
1994 in standard case	£30
1994 uncirculated decimal, 1994	£12
1995 gold Britannia, £100–£10 (4 coins)	BV
1996 gold, £5, £2 Peace, sovereign, half sovereign (4 coins)	BV
1996 gold, £2 Peace, sovereign, half sovereign (3 coins)	BV
1996 decimal, £2 Peace, £1 Welsh rev–1p (8 coins), deluxe case	£37
1996 in standard case	£30
1996 uncirculated decimal	£12
1996 gold Britannia, £100–£10 (4 coins)	BV
1996 gold, £5, £2, sovereign, half sovereign (4 coins)	BV
1996 gold, £2, sovereign, half sovereign (3 coins)	BV
1996 silver decimal, £1–1p (7 coins)	£90
1996 decimal, £5 60th Birthday, £2 Football,	

£1 Northern Irish rev–1p in deluxe case (9 coins)	£33
1996 in standard case	£30
1997 gold Britannia, £100–£10 (4 coins)	BV
1996 uncirculated decimal, £2–1p (8 coins)	£9
1997 gold, £5, £2 bimetal, sovereign, half sovereign (4 coins)	BV
1997 £2 bimetal, sovereign, half sovereign (3 coins)	BV
1997 silver Britannia, £2–20p	£110
1997 decimal, 50p, large and small size	£60
1997 Golden Wedding £5, £2 bimetal, £1 English rev–1p with new 50p in deluxe case	£35
1997 in standard case	£30
1997 uncirculated decimal, £2 bimetal, £1 English rev–1p with new 50p (9 coins)	£10
1998 gold Britannia, £100–£10 (4 coins)	BV
1998 silver Britannia, £2–20p	£110
1998 gold, £5–half sovereign	BV
1998 £2–half sovereign	BV
1998 decimal, Prince Charles, £5–1p in deluxe case	£38
1998 in standard case	£30
1998 uncirculated, as above, £2–1p (9 coins)	£12
1998 silver, EU and NHS 50p (2 coins)	£45
1999 gold Britannia, £100–£10 (4 coins)	BV
1999 £5, £2 Rugby World Cup, sovereign, half sovereign	BV
1999 £2 Rugby World Cup, sovereign, half sovereign	BV
1999 decimal, Diana £5–1p in deluxe case	£38
1999 in standard case	£30
1999 uncirculated, £2–1p (8 coins)	£12
2000 gold Britannia, £100–£10 (4 coins)	BV
2000 gold, £5–half sovereign	BV
2000 £2–half sovereign	BV
2000 decimal, £5–1p Maundy coins (13 coins)	£260
2000 executive (10 coins)	£60
2000 deluxe (10 coins)	£35
2000 standard (10 coins)	£26
2001 gold Britannia, £100–£10 (4 coins)	BV
2001 gold, £5, £2 Marconi Commemorative, sovereign, half sovereign (4 coins)	£3100
2001 £2 Marconi commemorative, sovereign, half sovereign (3 coins)	BV
2001 silver Britannia, new reverse designs, £2–20p	£85
2001 decimal, executive (10 coins)	£50
2001 deluxe (10 coins)	£34
2001 gift (10 coins)	£34
2001 standard (10 coins)	£30
2001 uncirculated, as above but no £5 (9 coins)	£14
2002 gold, £5–half sovereign, new reverse design	BV
2002 £2–half sovereign, new reverse design	BV
2002 Golden Jubilee £5, £2 bimetal, £1 (English rev)–1p plus Maundy coins (13 coins)	£9500
2002 Commonwealth Games £2, four reverses: England, Northern Ireland, Scotland and Wales	BV
2002 silver, Commonwealth Games, four reverses: £2 England, Northern Ireland, Scotland and Wales	£105
2002 gold Britannia, £100–£10 (4 coins)	BV
2002 silver piedfort, Commonwealth Games £2, four reverses: England, Northern Ireland, Scotland and Wales	£220
2002 decimal, Executive, Golden Jubilee £5,	

£2 bimetal, £1 English rev–1p (9 coins)	£60
2002 deluxe (9 coins)	£40
2002 gift (9 coins)	£35
2002 standard (9 coins)	£28
2002 uncirculated, 2002, £2 bimetal, £1 English rev–1p (8 coins)	£15
2002 uncirculated, Commonwealth Games £2, reverses: England, Northern Ireland, Scotland and Wales	£14
2003 gold, £5–half sovereign	BV
2003 £2 DNA–half sovereign	BV
2003 pattern set gold pounds (4 coins)	BV
2003 pattern set silver pounds (4 coins)	£85
2003 gold Britannia £100–£10 (4 coins)	BV
2003 silver Britannia £2–20p	£80
Gold set, mixed dates £100 (4 coins)	BV
Silver set, mixed dates £2 (4 coins)	£43
Silver set, mixed dates £2 (4 coins)	£43
Silver set, £5 (2 coins) different types	£55
2003 Silver set, £5–50p Coronation–Suffragette (5 coins)	£150
2003 decimal, executive (11 coins)	£60
2003 deluxe (11 coins)	£40
2003 standard (11 coins)	£30
2003 uncirculated (10 coins)	£12
2004 gold £5–half sovereign (4 coins)	BV
2004 gold, £2–half sovereign (3 coins)	BV
2004 pattern set, gold pounds (4 coins)	BV
2004 pattern set, silver pounds (4 coins)	£85
2004 silver set, £5–50p Entente Cordiale–Bannister (5 coins)	£130
2004 silver piedfort set, £2–50p Penydarren engine–Bannister (3 coins)	£125
2004 gold Britannia, £100–£10 (4 coins)	BV
2004 £50–£10	BV
2004 uncirculated set, 'new coin pack' (10 coins)	£10
2004 deluxe (10 coins)	£25
2004 executive (10 coins)	£45
2004 standard (10 coins)	£20
2005 gold, £5–half sovereign (4 coins)	BV
2005 £2–half sovereign (3 coins)	BV
2005 silver piedfort set, £2–50p Gunpowder Plot–Johnson's Dictionary (4 coins)	£150
2005 silver piedfort set, £5 (2 coins)	£115
2005 decimal, 2005, Executive (12 coins)	£68
2005 deluxe (12 coins)	£43
2005 standard (12 coins)	£32
2005 uncirculated (10 coins)	£13
2005 gold Britannia, £100–£10 (4 coins)	BV
2005 £50–£10 (3 coins)	BV
2005 silver Britannia, £2–20p (4 coins)	£85
2006 gold, £5–half sovereign (4)	BV
2006 £2–half sovereign (3 coins)	BV
2006 gold Britannia, £100–£10 (4 coins)	BV
2006 silver Britannia £2 gold plated, 5 different (5 coins)	£230
2006 gold, Brunel £2 (2 coins)	BV
2006 Victoria Cross 50p (2 coins)	BV
2006 silver, 80th Birthday (13 coins)	£280
2006 silver Britannia (5 coins)	£280
2006 Brunel £2 (2 coins)	£65
2006 silver piedfort, Brunel £2 (2 coins)	£85
2006 silver, 50p, Victoria Cross & Wounded Soldier (2 coins)	£55
2006 silver piedfort, 50 pence (2 coins)	£55
2006 silver piedfort, £5–50p 80th Birthday–Wounded Soldier (6 coins)	£285
2006 executive (13 coins)	£75
2006 deluxe (13 coins)	£50
2006 standard (13 coins)	£38
2007 gold, £5–half sovereign (4 coins)	BV
2007 £2–half sovereign (3 coins)	BV
2007 'Bridge' series (4 coins)	BV
2007 sovereign and half sovereign (2 coins)	BV
2007 platinum Britannia, £100–£10 (4 coins)	BV
2007 silver 'Bridge' series (4 coins)	£120
2007 decimal executive (12 coins)	£83
2007 deluxe (12 coins)	£53
2007 standard (12 coins)	£42
2007 uncirculated (9 coins)	£16
2008 gold Britannia, £100–£10 (4 coins)	BV
2008 gold, £5–half sovereign (4 coins)	BV
2008 gold £2–half sovereign (3 coins)	BV
2008 gold, sovereign and half sovereign (2 coins)	BV
2008 platinum Britannia, £100–£10 (4 coins)	BV
2008 platinum Royal Shield (7 coins)	BV
2008 platinum Emblems of Britain (7 coins)	BV
2008 platinum double set (14 coins)	BV
2008 gold Royal shield (7 coins)	BV
2008 gold Emblems of Britain (7 coins)	BV
2008 gold double set (14 coins)	BV
2008 silver Britannia, £100–£10 (4 coins)	BV
2008 silver Piedfort Royal Shield (6 coins)	£210
2008 silver Royal Shields (6 coins)	£153
2008 silver Emblems of Britain (6 coins)	£153
2008 silver double set (12 coins)	£285
2008 Family (5 coins)	£155
2008 commemorative piedfort (4)	£210
2008 decimal Royal Shields (6 coins)	BV
2008 decimal executive (11 coins)	£63
2008 deluxe (11 coins)	£42
2008 standard (11 coins)	£33
2008 uncirculated (9 coins)	£17
2008 uncirculated Emblems of Britain (9 coins)	£10
2008 Royal Shields (6 coins)	£33
2008 standard royal shields (6 coins)	£10
2008 double set (12 coins)	£20
2009 gold Britannia, £100–£10 (4 coins)	BV
2009 gold, £5–half sovereign (4 coins)	BV
2009 gold £2–half sovereign (3 coins)	BV
2009 silver Britannia, £2–20p	£105
2009 gold, sovereign and half sovereign (2 coins)	BV
2009 silver 50th Anniversary Mini (4 coins)	£155
2009 silver piedfort collection (4 coins)	£230
2009 silver family collection (6 coins)	£155
2009 silver set (12 coins)	£230
2009 decimal executive (12 coins)	£63
2009 deluxe (12 coins)	£42
2009 standard (12 coins)	£34
2009 uncirculated (11 coins)	£17

Sets beyond 2009 are not listed in this guide.

SCOTTISH COINS

SCOTTISH COINS

MINTS IN OPERATION IN SCOTLAND

The mints of the first coinage of Alexander III were the greatest number working together in Scotland, and therefore this area attracts collectors of the different mint issues.

For his reign, we give a price for issues of each mint town, but not for any other reign. From the reign of Mary, all Scottish coins were struck at Edinburgh.

MINT TOWN	KING
Aberdeen	Alexander III, David II, Robert III, James I, II, III
Ayr	Alexander III
Bamborough	Henry
Berwick	David I, Malcolm IV, William I, Alexander II, III, Robert Bruce, James III
Carlisle	David I, Henry
Corbridge	Henry
Dumbarton	Robert III
Dumfries	Alexander III
Dunbar	William I?, Alexander III

MINT TOWN	KING
Dundee	William I?, Alexander III
Dunfermline	William I
Forfar	Alexander III
Forres	Alexander III
Glasgow	Alexander III
Inverness	Alexander III
Jedburgh	Malcolm IV
Kelso	Alexander II
Kinghorn	Alexander III
Lanark	Alexander III
Linlithgow	James I, II
Montrose	Alexander III
Perth	William I, Alexander III, Robert II–James II
Renfrew	Alexander III
Roxburgh	Alexander III
St Andrews	Alexander III
Stirling	Alexander III, James I, II, Mary Stuart

Prices are for the commonest coins in each case.
For further details see *The Scottish Coinage*, by I Stewart
(Spink, 1967, reprint 1975) and *Coins of Scotland, Ireland
and The Islands* (Spink 2003).

DAVID I 1124–53	F	VF
Silver Pennies	£1250	£3000

Four different groups; struck at the mints of Berwick, Carlisle,
Roxborough and Edinburgh.

HENRY 1136–52
Earl of Huntingdon and Northumberland

	F	VF
Silver Pennies	£3000	£7000

Three types; struck at the mints of Corbridge, Carlisle and
Bamborough.

MALCOLM IV 1153–65

	F	VF
Silver Pennies	£5750	£12500

Five types; struck at the mints of Roxburgh and Berwick.

ABOVE: William the Lion Penny, Edinburgh

WILLIAM THE LION 1165–1214

	F	VF
Silver Pennies	£225	£650

Three issues; struck at the mints of Roxburgh, Berwick,
Edinburgh, Dun (Dunfermline?), Perth.

ALEXANDER II 1214–49

	F	VF
Silver Pennies	£875	£2500

Mints of Berwick and Roxburgh, varieties of bust.

ABOVE: Alexander III first coinage Penny

ALEXANDER III 1249–86
Transitional coinage 1249–50

Pennies	£500	*

First coinage silver Pennies 1250–80

Aberdeen	£200	£450
Ayr	£225	£500
Berwick	£140	£250
'DUN'	£275	£565
Edinburgh	£175	£350
Forfar	£485	£925
Fres	£400	£875
Glasgow	£225	£450
Inverness	£365	£750
Kinghorn	£525	£1350

	F	VF
Lanark	£350	£825
Montrose	£875	£1950
Perth	£140	£295
Renfrew	£775	£1875
Roxburgh	£140	£295
St Andrews	£350	£750
Stirling	£195	£495
'WILANERTER'	£600	£1475

ABOVE: Alexander III second coinage Halfpenny

Second coinage c1280

Silver Pennies	£45	£125
Halfpennies	£125	£350
Farthings	£350	£750

Many types and varieties.

JOHN BALLIOL 1292–6
First coinage, rough surface issue

Silver Pennies	£175	£485
Halfpennies	£400	£875

Second coinage, smooth surface issue

Silver Pennies	£145	£425
Halfpennies	£250	£600
Farthing	£1750	*

ROBERT BRUCE 1306–29

Silver Pennies	£825	£1950
Halfpennies	£1250	£3500
Farthings	£1750	£4000

Probably all struck at Berwick.

ABOVE: David II Halfgroat

DAVID II 1329–71

		ext. rare
Gold Nobles		
Silver Groats	£195	£495
Halfgroats	£195	£495
Pennies	£85	£200
Halfpennies	£450	£1100
Farthings	£775	£1850

Three issues, but these denominations were not struck for all
issues. Edinburgh and Aberdeen mints.

	F	VF
ROBERT II 1371–90		
Silver Groats	£185	£465
Halfgroats	£165	£485
Pennies	£135	£475
Halfpennies	£185	£475

Some varieties. Struck at Dundee, Edinburgh and Perth.

ROBERT III 1390–1406

Gold Lion or Crowns	£2850	£5500
Demy-lions or Halfcrowns	£1650	£3850
Silver groats	£135	£385
Halfgroats	£225	£600
Pennies	£425	£1250
Halfpennies	£400	£850

Three issues, many varieties. Struck at mints of Edinburgh, Aberdeen, Perth and Dumbarton.

ABOVE: James I Demy

JAMES I 1406–37

Gold Demies	£1850	£4850
Half-demies	£1950	£5000
Silver Groats	£250	£650
Billon Pennies	£300	£850
Billon Halfpennies	£500	£1500

Mints: Aberdeen, Edinburgh, Inverness, Linlithgow, Perth and Stirling.

JAMES II 1437–60

Gold Demies from	£1750	£3500
Lions from	£2950	£6500
Half lions	£3650	£7500
Silver Groats	£300	£800
Halfgroats	£850	£1750
Billon Pennies	£400	£1250

Two issues, many varieties. Mints: Aberdeen, Edinburgh, Linlithgow, Perth, Roxburgh and Stirling.

ECCLESIASTICAL ISSUES c1452–80

Bishop Kennedy copper Pennies	£140	£365
Copper Farthings	£295	£800

Different types and varieties.

JAMES III 1460–88

Gold Riders	from	£3750	£7500
Half-riders		£4000	£8250
Quarter-riders		£5250	*
Unicorns		£3750	£9250
Silver Groats	from	£500	£975

ABOVE: James IIII Groat

		F	VF
Halfgroats	from	£950	£2850
Pennies	from	£400	£850
Billon Placks	from	£100	£275
Half-Placks	from	£140	£395
Pennies	from	£185	£500
Halfpennies		ext.rare	
Copper Farthings	from	£600	*

Many varieties. Mints: Aberdeen, Berwick and Edinburgh.

ABOVE: James IV Unicorn

JAMES IV 1488–1513

Gold Unicorns		£2500	£6000
Half-unicorns		£2000	£4850
Lions or Crowns		£4250	£10500
Half-lions		£4750	£11500
Pattern Angel		unique	
Silver Groats	from	£625	£1725
Halfgroats		£700	£2000
Pennies, light coinage		ext. rare	*
Billon Placks		£45	£150
Half-placks		£125	£400
Pennies		£70	£165

Different types and varieties. Mint: Edinburgh.

ABOVE: James V 1540 'Bonnet' piece

JAMES V 1513-42

		F	VF
Gold Unicorns		£3000	£8500
Half-unicorns		£3750	£8500
Crowns		£1950	£4750
'Bonnet' pieces or Ducats		£7500	£17500
Two-thirds ducats		£8500	*
One-third ducats		£7000	*
Silver Groats	from	£400	£950
One-third groats		£265	£750

ABOVE: James V Groat

	F	VF
Billon Placks	£35	£110
Bawbees	£30	£110
Half-bawbees	£95	£300
Quarter-bawbees		unique

Different issues and varieties. Mint: Edinburgh.

MARY 1542-67

First period 1542-58

	F	VF
Gold Crown	£4250	£11000
Twenty Shillings	£5500	£13750
Lions or Forty-four Shillings	£4000	£9000

ABOVE: Mary three pound piece or ryal

	F	VF
Half-lions or Twenty-two shillings	£2750	£7500
Ryals or Three Pound pieces, 1555, 1557, 1558	£12500	£30000
Half-ryals 1555, 1557, 1558	£13500	*
Portrait Testoons, 1553	£12500	*
Non-portrait Testoons, 1555-58	£350	£900
Half-testoons, 1555-58	£300	£800
Billon Bawbees	£45	£125
Half-bawbees	£65	£175
Pennies, facing bust	£350	£1100
No bust 1556	£225	£750
Lions, 1555, 1558	£30	£125
Placks, 1557	£45	£125

Second period, Francis and Mary, 1558-60

	F	VF
Gold Ducats or Sixty shillings		ext. rare
Non-portrait Testoons, 1558-61	£350	£925
Half-testoons, 1558-60	£275	£750
Twelvepenny groats, Nonsunt, 1558-9	£75	£225
Lions, 1559-60	£35	£120

Third period, widowhood, 1560-5

	F	VF
Gold Crown 1561		ext. rare
Portrait Testoons, 1561-2	£4750	£12000
Half-testoons, 1561-2	£4250	£11000

Fourth period, Henry and Mary, 1565-7

	F	VF
Portrait Ryals, 1565		ext. rare
Non-portrait Ryals, 1565-7	£750	£2000

ABOVE: Mary and Henry Darnley 1566 Ryal

	F	VF
Two-third ryals, 1565-7	£525	£1450
Two-third ryals, undated	£1875	£4750
One-third ryals, 1565-6	£600	£1500
Testoon, 1565		ext. rare

Fifth period, 2nd widowhood, 1567

	F	VF
Non-portrait Ryals, 1567	£750	£2000
Two-thirds ryal, 1567	£850	£2250
One-thirds ryals, 1566-7	£700	£1725

Mints: Edinburgh, Stirling (but only for some bawbees).

JAMES VI
Before English accession 1567-1603
First coinage 1567-71

	F	VF
Ryals 1567-71	£485	£1500
Two-third ryals	£375	£925
One-third ryals	£400	£950

Second coinage 1571-80

	F	VF
Gold Twenty Pounds pieces	£42500	£85000
Silver half merks or nobles, 1572-77, 1580	£135	£425
Quarter merks or half nobles	£110	£325

	F	VF
Two merks, 1578–80	£2850	£6500
Merks, 1579–80	£3500	*

Third coinage 1580–81

	F	VF
Gold Ducats, 1580	£10000	£27500
Sixteen shillings, 1581	£3750	£8000
Eight shillings, 1581	£2850	£6750
Four shillings, 1581	£4250	*
Two shillings, 1581		ext. rare

Fourth coinage 1582–88

	F	VF
Gold Lion Nobles	£15000	ext. rare
Two-third lion nobles	£12750	£32500
One-third lion nobles	£8750	£22500
Silver Forty shillings, 1582	£7500	£20000
Thirty shillings, 1582–86	£625	£2000
Twenty shillings, 1582–85	£500	£1650
Ten shillings, 1582–84	£395	£1350

ABOVE: James VI 1582 Ten Shillings

Fifth coinage 1588

	F	VF
Gold Thistle nobles	£5000	£12500

Sixth coinage 1591–93

	F	VF
Gold Hat pieces, 1591–93	£9500	£25000
Silver Balance half-merks, 1591–93	£400	£875
Balance quarter merks, 1591	£675	£1825

Seventh coinage 1594–1601

	F	VF
Gold Riders	£1675	£5250
Half Riders	£1700	£5000
Silver Ten Shillings, 1593–95, 1598–1601	£150	£450
Five shillings, 1593–5, 1598–1601	£135	£500

ABOVE: James VI seventh coinage 1593 Five shillings

	F	VF
Thirty-pence pieces 1595–6, 1598–9, 1601	£150	£375
Twelve-pence piece 1594–6	£135	£275

ABOVE: James VI 1603 Sword and Sceptre piece

Eighth coinage 1601–4

	F	VF
Gold Sword and Sceptre pieces	£950	£2650
Half sword and sceptre pieces	£700	£1625
Silver Thistle-merks, 1601–4	£100	£500
Half thistle-merks	£75	£265
Quarter thistle-merks	£65	£200
Eighth thistle-merks, 1601–3	£45	£125

Billon and copper issues

	F	VF
Billon Placks or Eightpenny groats	£20	£90
Half-placks	£135	£400
Hardheads	£40	£150
Saltire Placks	£200	£525
Copper Twopence 1597	£95	£325
Penny 1597	£600	*

After English accession 1603–25

	F	VF
Gold Units	£1200	£3000
Double Crowns	£1850	£4250
Britain Crowns	£700	£1650
Halfcrowns	£575	£1375
Thistle Crowns	£400	£1000
Silver Sixty shillings	£575	£1750
Thirty shillings	£125	£400
Twelve shillings	£135	£400
Six shillings	£500	£1750
Two shillings	£40	£125
One shilling	£65	£165
Sixpences	*	*
Copper Twopences	£20	£60
Pennies	£135	£375

CHARLES I 1625–49
First coinage 1625–36

	F	VF
Gold Units	£1500	£3850
Double Crowns	£3000	£8250
Britain Crowns	ext. rare	
Milled Angel	ext. rare	
Silver Sixty shillings	£875	£2950
Thirty shillings	£150	£450
Twelve shillings	£285	£725
Six shillings	£425	£1500
Two shillings	£65	£165
One shilling	£85	£250

Second coinage 1636	F	VF
Half–merks	£70	£175
Forty–pence pieces	£70	£175
Twenty–pence pieces	£65	£150

Third coinage 1637–42		
Gold Units	£2500	£6000
Half–units	£1150	£4250
Britain Crowns	£1650	£4250
Britain Halfcrowns	£925	£2250
Silver Sixty shillings	£800	££2250
Thirty shillings	£150	£450

ABOVE: Charles II first coinage 1669 Merk

ABOVE: Charles I third coinage Briot's issue twelve shillings

	F	VF
Twelve shillings	£110	£300
Six shillings	£90	£225
Half–merks	£90	£225
Forty–pence piece	£35	£100
Twenty–pence piece	£30	£80
Three shillings	£65	£175
Two shillings	£50	£125
Copper twopences, lion	£20	£50
Pennies	£300	*
Twopences, CR crowned	£15	£35
Twopences, Stirling turners	£15	£35

CHARLES II 1660–85
First coinage

	F	VF
Silver Four merks, 1664 thistle above bust	£850	£3000
1664 thistle below bust	£875	£2750
1665	£4000	*
1670	£900	£2250
1673	£800	£2750
1674 F below bust	£800	£2750
1675	£800	£2750
Two merks, 1664 thistle above bust	£485	£1425
1664 thistle below bust	£485	£1425
1670	£485	£1425
1673	£485	£1425
1673 F below bust	ext.rare	
1674	£485	£1425
1674 F below bust	£500	£1750
1675	£385	£1350
Merks, 1664	£110	£375
1665	£125	£485
1666	£275	£750

	F	VF
1668	£265	£700
1669	£80	£300
1670	£80	£300
1671	£80	£325
1672	£90	£325
1673	£80	£300
1674	£150	£495
1674 F below bust	£120	£375
1675 F below bust	£120	£375
1675	£225	£625
Half–merks, 1664	£175	£500
1665	£250	£675
1666	£295	£700
1667	£225	£700
1668	£225	£725
1669	£90	£350
1670	£90	£350
1671	£100	£325
1672	£100	£325
1673	£120	£400
1675 F below bust	£110	£375
1675	£140	£475

ABOVE: Charles II second coinage 1676 Dollar

Second coinage

	F	VF
Silver Dollars, 1676	£550	£1750
1679	£585	£1800
1680	£725	£2350
1681	£585	£1800
1682	£425	£1650
Half–dollars, 1675	£450	£1325
1676	£525	£1650

	F	VF
1681	£450	£1425
Quarter–dollars, 1675	£135	£475
1676	£120	£350
1677	£120	£375
1678	£125	£450
1679	£135	£475
1680	£120	£375
1681	£120	£375
1682	£125	£425
Eighth–dollars, 1676	£85	£300
1677	£85	£300
1678/7	£175	£575
1679	£250	£600
1680	£80	£275
1682	£250	£600
Sixteenth–dollars, 1677	£65	£225
1678/7	£75	£275
1679/7	£100	£375
1680	£225	£575
1681	£70	£275
Copper twopence, CR crowned	£20	£70
Bawbees, 1677–9	£75	£275
Turners, 1677–9	£50	£150

JAMES VII 1685–9

Silver sixty shillings, 1688, proof only	FDC	£3000
Gold proof only	FDC	£90000

Struck in 1828, not contemporary.

	F	VF
Silver forty shillings, 1687	£350	£1000
1688	£250	£1000
Ten shillings, 1687	£135	£500
1688	£225	£700

WILLIAM AND MARY 1689–94

	F	VF
Sixty shillings, 1691	£650	£2000
1692	£650	£1950
Forty shillings, 1689	£250	£850
1690	£250	£695
1691	£200	£595
1692	£175	£550
1693	£175	£550
1694	£250	£695
Twenty shillings, 1693	£485	£1425
1694	£600	£1625
Ten shillings, 1689	*	*
1690	£275	£750
1691	£150	£495
1692	£150	£495
1694	£240	£675
Five shillings, 1691	£175	£425
1694	£175	£425
Copper Bawbees, 1691–4	£110	£425
Bodles, 1691–4	£35	£120

WILLIAM II 1694–1702

	F	VF
Gold Pistole 1701	£6000	£12500
Half–pistole, 1701	£4500	£10000

	F	VF
Silver sixty shillings, 1699	*	*
Forty shillings, 1695	£195	£500
1696	£200	£525
1697	£250	£600
1698	£250	£625
1699	£250	£625
1700	ext. rare	
Twenty shillings, 1695	£225	£725
1696	£195	£725
1697	£325	£1000
1698	£175	£725
1698/7	£225	£700
1699	£375	£1150

ABOVE: William III 1696 Ten shillings

	F	VF
Ten shillings, 1695	£165	£425
1696	£165	£425
1697	£175	£585
1698	£175	£485
1699	£185	£500
Five shillings, 1695	£100	£275
1696	£90	£250
1697	£90	£250
1699	£90	£250
1700	£90	£250
1701	£110	£400
1702	£125	£400
Copper Bawbees, 1695–7	£85	£375
Bodles, 1695–7	£50	£160

ANNE 1702–14
Pre–Union 1702–7

	F	VF
Ten shillings, 1705	£150	£425
1706	£150	£400
Five shillings, 1705	£60	£165
1706	£60	£165

JAMES VIII 1688–1766 The Old Pretender

Gold Guinea 1716	FDC	£15000
Silver	FDC	£1650
Bronze	FDC	£1350
Crown 1709		unique
Crown 1716, silver	FDC	£3500
Gold		ext. rare
Bronze		ext. rare

The 1716–dated pieces were struck in 1828 from the original dies.

IRISH COINS

■ **HAMMERED ISSUES 995–1661**

Most of the Irish coins of this period are in fairly poor condition and it is difficult to find specimens in VF condition or better.

For more details see *The Guide Book to the Coinage of Ireland AD 995 to the Present Day* by Anthony Dowle or Spink's *Coins of Scotland, Ireland & the Islands* by Patrick Finn (Spink 2002) and *Irish Coin Values* by Patrick Finn (Spink 1979). Prices are for the commonest coins in each case.

HIBERNO–NORSE OF DUBLIN 995–1150
This series runs from Phase I to Phase VII and prices quoted are for the commonest type of each phase.

		F	VF
Silver Pennies, imitative of English coins, many types and varieties			
Phase 1	from	£500	£2000
Phase 2	from	£425	£750
Phase 3	from	£250	£500
Phase 4	from	£425	£975
Phase 5	from	£700	£2000
Phase 6	from	£400	£1100
Phase 7	from	£1250	£3750

ABOVE: Hiberno–Norse phase II Penny

ABOVE: Hiberno–Norse phase IV Penny

JOHN AS LORD OF IRELAND c1185–1199

	F	VF
Silver Halfpennies, profile portrait	£3500	*
Facing head	£200	£525
Farthings	£725	£1900

Different types, varieties, mints and moneyers.

JOHN DE COURCY LORD OF ULSTER 1177–1205

		F	VF
Silver Penny		ext. rare	
Halfpenny		£2500	£6750
Farthings	from	£1500	£4500

Different types, varieties, mints and moneyers.

JOHN AS KING OF ENGLAND AND LORD OF IRELAND c1199–1216

Rex/Triangle types		F	VF
Silver Pennies	from	£70	£150
Halfpennies		£110	£325
Farthings		£500	£1250

Different types, varieties, mints and moneyers.

HENRY III 1216–1272

		F	VF
Silver Pennies, c 1251–1254	from	£65	£175

Dublin only, moneyers DAVI and RICHARD, many varieties.

ABOVE: Edward I Waterford Penny

EDWARD I 1272–1307
First coinage, 1276–79

	F	VF
Pennies	£1500	£4750

Second coinage, 1279–1302

	F	VF
Silver Pennies from	£50	£140
Halfpennies	£75	£225

ABOVE: Edward I Farthing Dublin

	F	VF
Farthings	£135	£375

Dublin, Waterford and Cork, many different issues.

EDWARD III 1327–1377

	F	VF
Silver Halfpennies Dublin mint	£3250	*
Silver Farthing Dublin mint	£3000	*

HENRY VI 1422–1461

	F	VF
Silver Pennies, Dublin mint	£4250	*

ABOVE: Edward IV untitled crown type Groat

EDWARD IV 1461–1483

		F	VF
Silver untitled crown Groats	from	£1250	£3500
Pennies		£1500	*
Halfpenny		ext. rare	
Cross on rose/sun Groats		£3250	£9250
Pennies		£1500	£4250
Titled crown Groats		£2750	£6750
Halfgroats		£3000	*
Pennies		£2250	*
Cross & pellets Groats		£325	£700
Halfgroats		£100	£250
Halfpenny		£500	£1500
Bust/rose–sun Double Groats		£3000	£8000
Groats		£2500	£6250
Halfgroats		£2500	*
Pennies		£1850	*
Copper crown/cross Farthing		£1500	£3250
Half–farthings		£1625	£3500

PATRICIUS/SALVATOR 1463–65

	F	VF
Silver Farthing	£1750	£3850
Three crowns/sun Half–farthings	£1500	£3750

HENRY VI Restored 1470–1471

Groats	ext. rare

EDWARD IV Second reign 1471–83

		F	VF
'English style' Groats	from	£300	£700
Halfgroats		£750	£1825
Pennies		£60	£225
Halfpenny		£525	£1500
Ungoverned mints, c. 1470–77			
Groats	from	£650	£1750
Halfgroats		£1500	£3500
Pennies		£285	£750

Suns and roses/rose on cross coinage

	F	VF
Groat	£750	£2000
Pennies	£350	£1500

This is an abbreviated listing of the issues of Edward IV which are numerous. There are also many varieties and different mints.

EDWARD V April–June 1483

	F	VF
Groats	£750	£1825
Pennies	£1100	£3000

ABOVE: Richard III 'three crowns' Groat

RICHARD III 1483–1485

		F	VF
Silver bust/rose–cross Groats	from	£2350	£4950

		F	VF
Halfgroats			unique
Pennies		£3000	£7250
Cross and pellet pennies		£1650	£4000
Three–crown Groats		£800	£1975
Different mints and varieties.			

ABOVE: Henry VII early 'three crowns' groat

ABOVE: Henry VII facing bust Groat, Dublin

HENRY VII 1485–1509

Early issues	F	VF
Three–crown Groats	£225	£585
Halfgroats	£350	£925
Pennies	£875	£2250
Halfpennies	£1750	*

Later issues		
Facing bust Groats	£250	£675
Halfgroats	£1000	£3000
Pennies	£1100	£2950
Crowned H Pennies	£2000	*

Many varieties. Mints: mainly Dublin, Waterford issues are extremely rare.

LAMBERT SIMNEL, Pretender 1487

	F	VF
Three–crown Groats	£1850	£5250
Different mints and varieties.		

HENRY VIII 1509–1547

	F	VF
Silver 'harp' Groats	£250	£525
Halfgroats	£2000	£4500

These harped coins carry crowned initials, such as HA (Henry and Anne Boleyn), HI (Henry and Jane Seymour), HK (Henry and Katherine Howard) or HR (Henricus Rex).

Posthumous issues

	F	VF
Portrait Groats current for 6 pence	£200	£725
Halfgroats current for 3 pence	£250	£825
Pennies current for 3 halfpence	£550	£1650
Halfpennies current for 3 farthings	£925	£2750

ABOVE: Henry VIII posthumous portrait Groat

Different busts and mintmarks.

EDWARD VI 1547–1553

Base Shillings 1552 (MDLII)	£925	£3500
Contemporary copy	£50	£225

ABOVE: Mary 1553 Shilling

MARY 1553–1558

	F	VF
Shillings 1553 (MDLIII)	£975	£3850
1554 (MDLIIII)	£3000	£7250
Groats		ext. rare
Halfgroats		ext. rare
Pennies		ext. rare

Several varieties of the shillings and groats.

PHILIP AND MARY 1554–1558

Base Shillings	£500	£1950
Groats	£100	£495

Several minor varieties.

ELIZABETH I 1558–1603

Base portrait Shillings	£475	£1650
Groats	£120	£575
Fine silver portrait Shillings 1561	£450	£1350
Groats	£475	£1650
Base shillings arms–harp	£175	£625
Sixpences	£125	£475
Threepences	£850	*
Pennies	£45	£150
Halfpennies	£75	£300

JAMES I 1603–1625

Silver shillings	£125	£525
Sixpences	£90	£375

Different issues, busts and mintmarks.

Siege money of the Irish Rebellion 1642–1649

Siege coins are rather irregular in size and shape.

CHARLES I 1625–1649
Kilkenny Money 1642

Copper Halfpennies F	£625	£1875
Copper Farthings F	£625	*

Inchiquin Money 1642–1646
The only gold coins struck in Ireland. **from**

Gold Double Pistole		ext. rare
Gold Pistole F	£65000	*
Silver Crowns	£3750	£6850
Halfcrowns	£3250	£5500
Shillings	£2500	£7000

	F	VF
Ninepences	£6500	*
Sixpences	£5750	*
Groats F	£6000	£13000
Threepences		ext. rare

Three issues and many varieties.

Ormonde Money 1643

Crowns F	from	£650	£1500
Halfcrowns F		£485	£975
Shillings		£225	£500
Sixpences F		£175	£450
Groats F		£200	£400
Threepences		£175	£450
Halfgroats F		£700	£1500

Many varieties.

ABOVE: Ormonde Money Halfcrown

ABOVE: Ormonde Money Sixpence

Rebel Money 1643

Crowns	£4250	£13000
Halfcrowns	£4500	£13750

Town Pieces 1645–1647
Bandon

Copper Farthings F	£975	*

Kinsale

Copper Farthings F	£500	*

Youghal

Copper Farthings F	£500	£1750
Brass Twopences		ext. rare
Pewter Threepences		ext. rare

Cork

Silver Shillings F	£6000	£13000
Sixpences F	£1650	£3500
Copper Halfpennies	£1500	*
Copper Farthings F	£1000	*
Elizabeth I Shillings countermarked CORKE F		ext. rare

ABOVE: Cork 1647 Sixpence

'Blacksmith's' Money 1649
Based on English Tower Halfcrown.

Halfcrown, varieties	£875	£2500

Dublin Money 1649

Crowns	£5250	£12500
Halfcrowns	£3750	£8750

◼ CHARLES II TO GEORGE IV

All the issues of this series except Bank of Ireland tokens were struck in base metal.

The series features a large number of varieties, but there is space here for only the main types and best-known variants. A number of rare proofs have also been omitted.

Except for the 'gunmoney' of James II, Irish copper coins are hard to find in the top grades, especially the so-called 'Voce Populi' issues and specimens of Wood's coinage.

We have listed some of the 'gunmoney' of James II in only three grades – Fair, Fine and VF. The majority of these hastily produced coins were not well-struck and pieces with little substantial wear are, arguably, not Extremely Fine.

Dating of gunmoney: in the calendar used up to 1723, the legal or civil year started on March 25 in Great Britain and Ireland, so December 1689 came before, not after January, February and March 1689. Coins dated March 1689 and March 1690 were struck in the same month.

CHARLES II	Fair	F	VF	EF
Armstrong issues				
1660–1661				
Copper Farthings	£15	£30	£150	*
St Patrick's coinage				
Halfpennies	£875	£2000	*	*
Star in rev legend	£1100	*	*	*
Farthings	£150	£475	*	*
Stars in rev legend	£200	£600	*	*
Cloud around				
St Patrick	£225	£700	*	*
Martlet below king	£200	£600	*	*
Annulet below king	£200	£600	*	*

ABOVE: Charles II St Patrick's Farthing

Regal coinage	Fair	F	VF	EF
Halfpennies, 1680,				
large letters, small cross	£15	£50	£250	*
1680 pellets	£15	£50	£250	*
1681 large letters	£15	£50	£250	*
1681 small letters	£50	£185	*	*
1682 large letters	£15	£50	£250	*
1682 small letters	£15	£50	£250	£1500
1683	£15	£50	£250	£1500
1684	£25	£95	£400	*
JAMES II				
Regular coinage				
Halfpennies, 1685	£20	£65	£275	*
1686	£20	£65	£275	*
1687	£125	£450	*	*
1688	£20	£85	£300	*
Emergency coinage, 'Gunmoney'				
Crowns, 1690	£50	£100	£265	£750
1690 horseman, sword				
to E of REX	£125	£225	£550	£1350

ABOVE: James II 1690 'Gunmoney' Crown

	Fair	F	VF	EF
Large Halfcrowns,				
1689 July	£15	£60	£195	£500
1689 August	£10	£40	£165	£425
1689 September	£8	£35	£150	£450
1689 October	£8	£35	£150	£450
1689 November	£10	£40	£125	£450
1689 December	£10	£40	£150	£450
1689 January	£10	£40	£150	£400
1689 February	£8	£35	£150	£450
1689 March	£8	£35	£150	£450
1690 March	£8	£35	£150	£450
1690 April	£8	£35	£150	£450
1690 May	£10	£40	£150	£400
Small Halfcrowns				
1690 April	£20	£75	£375	£895
1690 May	£10	£30	£170	£450
1690 June	£10	£35	£195	£450
1690 July	£10	£35	£165	£500
1690 August	£12	£40	£175	£685
1690 September	*	*	*	*
1690 October	£35	£110	£485	*
Large Shillings, 1689 July	£8	£25	£95	£300
1689 August	£6	£20	£80	£275
1689 September	£6	£20	£70	£275
1689 October	£8	£25	£95	£300
1689 November	£6	£20	£75	£275
1689 December	£6	£20	£70	£265
1689 January	£6	£20	£70	£265
1689 February	£6	£20	£70	£265
1689 March	£7	£20	£70	£275
1690 March	£8	£25	£70	£275
1690 April	£8	£25	£90	£300
Small Shillings,1690 April	£10	£30	£125	£350
1690 May	£7	£20	£90	£300
1690 June	£7	£20	£80	£300
1690 July	*	*	*	*
1690 August	*	*	*	*
1690 September	£125	£300	*	*

	Fair	F	VF	EF
Sixpences, 1689 June	£10	£40	£120	£325
1689 July	£8	£35	£110	£275
1689 August	£8	£35	£110	£275
1689 September	£10	£40	£135	£575
1689 October	*	*	*	*
1689 November	£8	£35	£110	£300
1689 December	£8	£35	£110	£275
1689 January	£10	£40	£120	£300
1689 February	£8	£35	£110	£300
1689 March	*	*	*	*
1690 March	*	*	*	*
1690 April	*	*	*	*
1690 May	£15	£50	£150	*
1690 June	*	*	*	*
1690 October	*	*	*	*

Pewter Money

	Fair	F	VF	EF
Crowns	£900	£2500	£4950	*
Groats	£750	£1650	*	*
Pennies large bust	£500	£1500	*	*
Small bust	£475	£975	*	*
Halfpennies large bust	£125	£350	£900	*
Halfpennies small bust	£90	£295	£750	£2500

ABOVE: Limerick Money Halfpenny

Limerick Money	Fair	F	VF	EF
Halfpennies	£20	£65	£225	£525
Farthings reversed N	£35	£90	£295	*
Normal N	£45	£100	£300	*

WILLIAM AND MARY				
Halfpennies, 1692	£9	£40	£225	*
1693	£9	£40	£225	*
1694	£12	£50	£225	*

WILLIAM III				
Halfpennies, 1696				
draped bust	£15	£65	£285	£1500
Halfpennies 1696 crude				
undraped bust	£40	£250	£700	*

GEORGE I				
Wood's coinage				
Halfpennies, 1722 harp left	£18	£65	£385	£1325
1722 harp right	£12	£35	£200	£675
1723	£10	£30	£135	£550
1723 obv Rs altered Bs	£12	£35	£135	£550
1723 no stop after date	£12	£35	£135	£550
1723/2	£10	£35	£150	£600

	Fair	F	VF	EF
1723 star in rev legend	*	*	*	*
1723 no stop before HIBERNIA	£10	£30	£135	£600
1724 head divided rev legend	£10	£30	£165	£685
1724 legend continuous over head	£15	£40	£175	*
Farthings 1722 harp left	£100	£400	£1350	*
1723 D: G:	£45	£125	£500	£2000
1723 DEI GRATIA	£10	£35	£135	£485
1724	£12	£50	£165	£625

	Fair	F	VF	EF
GEORGE II				
Halfpennies, 1736	*	£10	£50	£425
1737	*	£10	£50	£425
1738	£1	£12	£70	£450
1741	*	£10	£50	£425
1742	*	£10	£50	£425
1743	£2	£15	£60	£425
1744	£1	£12	£70	£485
1744/3	£2	£15	£60	£425
1746	£1	£12	£60	£425
1747	*	£10	£70	£425
1748	£2	£12	£65	£475
1749	*	£10	£50	£425
1750	*	£10	£45	£425
1751	*	£10	£45	£425
1752	*	£10	£45	£425
1753	*	£12	£50	£425
1760	*	£10	£40	£395
Farthings, 1737	£1	£12	£65	£485
1738	*	£10	£50	£425
1744	*	£10	£45	£425
1760	*	£8	£40	£350

	Fair	F	VF	EF
Voce populi coinage				
Halfpennies, 1760, Type 1	£35	£150	£425	*
Type 2	£5	£175	£350	*
Type 3	£75	£175	£400	*
Type 4	£60	£150	£325	*
Type 5	£60	£150	£300	*
Type 6	£60	£150	£300	£1500
Type 7	£60	£160	£350	£1600
Type 8	£60	£150	£300	*
Type 9	£75	£175	£400	*
Type 9, P before head	£25	£100	£300	£1500
Type 9, P under head	£25	£100	£300	£1500
Farthings, 1760, Type 1 loop to truncation	£75	£250	£1250	£3500
Type 2 no loop	*	*	*	*

	Fair	F	VF	EF
GEORGE III				
London coinage				
Halfpennies, 1766	*	£15	£65	£325
11769	*	£15	£65	£325
1769 2nd type	*	£20	£85	£385
1775	*	£20	£85	£385
1776	£5	£35	£100	£575
1781	*	£15	£65	£325
1782	*	£15	£65	£325

	F	VF	EF	Unc
Soho coinage				
Penny 1805	*	£30	£125	£350
Halfpenny 1805	*	£15	£85	£195
Farthing 1806	*	£12	£50	£195

Bank of Ireland token coinage 1804 Six shillings

	Fair	F	VF	EF
Bank of Ireland token coinage				
Silver Six shillings 1804	£85	£225	£450	£950
Thirty pence 1808	£25	£55	£110	£400
Ten pence 1805	*	£10	£30	£100
Ten pence 1806	*	£10	£30	£100
Ten pence 1813	*	£10	£30	£100
Five pence 1805	*	£10	£25	£85
Five pence 1806	*	£10	£30	£100

	F	VF	EF	Unc
GEORGE IV				
Penny 1822	£8	£40	£175	£425
1823	£10	£60	£200	£465
Halfpenny 1822	£5	£15	£110	£265
1823	£5	£15	£125	£275

ABOVE: George IV proof penny, 1822

FREE STATE AND REPUBLIC

Proofs exist for nearly all dates of the modern Irish coinage. However, only a few dates have become available to collectors or dealers and apart from the 1928 proofs, are all very rare. They have therefore been omitted from the list.

TEN SHILLINGS

	F	VF	EF	Unc
1966	*	£2	£6	£20
1966 proof	*	*	*	£30

HALFCROWNS

	F	VF	EF	Unc
1928	*	£8	£20	£60
1928 proof	*	*	*	£85
1930	*	£30	£225	£465
1931	£8	£30	£200	£425
1933	*	£25	£175	£500
1934	*	£20	£100	£300
1937	£35	£100	£725	£1950
1938	*	*	*	*
1939	*	£5	£25	£80
1940	*	£6	£20	£95
1941	*	£6	£25	£85
1942	*	£4	£20	£75
1943	£70	£150	£850	£2750
1951	*	*	£6	£40
1954	*	*	£7	£45
1955	*	*	£5	£25
1959	*	*	£4	£20
1961	*	*	£5	£15
1961 mule normal obv/pre-1939 rev	£8	£20	£300	£725
1962	*	*	*	£5
1963	*	*	*	£10
1964	*	*	*	£5
1966	*	*	*	£10
1967	*	*	*	£3

FLORINS

	F	VF	EF	Unc
1928	*	£5	£18	£40
1928 proof	*	*	*	£60
1930	*	£15	£145	£425
1931	£5	£35	£185	£425
1933	£8	£18	£185	£425
1934	£12	£60	£385	£1000
1935	*	£10	£125	£325
1937	£5	£18	£185	£365
1939	*	£4	£10	£50
1940	*	£5	£12	£50
1941	*	£5	£20	£85
1942	*	£5	£12	£60
1943	£3850	£8000	£15000	£30000
1951	*	*	£3	£25
1954	*	*	£3	£20
1955	*	*	£3	£20
1959	*	*	£3	£20
1961	*	*	£6	£40
1962	*	*	£3	£18
1963	*	*	£3	£18
1964	*	*	*	£5
1965	*	*	*	£5
1966	*	*	*	£5
1968	*	*	*	£5

SHILLINGS

	F	VF	EF	Unc
1928	*	£3	£8	£30
1928 proof	*	*	*	£45
1930	£7	£20	£145	£425
1931	*	£15	£65	£275
1933	£5	£10	£80	£265
1935	*	£5	£40	£135
1937	£10	£25	£400	£1000
1939	*	£3	£8	£35
1940	*	£3	£12	£40
1941	*	£5	£15	£45
1942	*	£5	£8	£28
1951	*	*	£3	£20
1954	*	*	£3	£15
1955	*	*	£3	£18
1959	*	*	£6	£25
1962	*	*	*	£5
1963	*	*	*	£4
1964	*	*	*	£5
1966	*	*	*	£4
1968	*	*	*	£4

SIXPENCES

	F	VF	EF	Unc
1928	*	*	£3	£25
1928 proof	*	*	*	£30
1934	*	*	£12	£100
1935	*	£3	£18	£165
1939	*	*	£5	£35
1940	*	*	£5	£25
1942	*	*	£5	£25
1945	*	£8	£40	£200
1946	£5	£12	£85	£475
1947	*	£6	£25	£135

IRISH COINS

IRISH COINS

Year	F	VF	EF	Unc
1948	*	£2	£8	£35
1949	*	*	£5	£30
1950	*	£15	£35	£185
1952	*	*	£4	£20
1953	*	*	£5	£22
1955	*	*	£4	£18
1956	*	*	£3	£12
1958	*	*	£5	£40
1959	*	*	£2	£7
1960	*	*	£2	£7
1961	*	*	£2	£7
1962	*	*	£3	£30
1964	*	*	*	£3
1965	*	*	*	£3
1966	*	*	*	£3
1967	*	*	*	£3
1968	*	*	*	£2
1969	*	*	*	£3

THREEPENCES

Year	F	VF	EF	Unc
1928	*	*	£3	£18
1928 proof	*	*	£3	£25
1933	*	£5	£60	£250
1934	*	£3	£15	£65
1935	*	£5	£25	£175
1939	*	£5	£60	£195
1940	*	*	£10	£40
1942	*	*	£5	£35
1943	*	*	£8	£75
1946	*	*	£5	£30
1948	*	£2	£15	£80
1949	*	*	£5	£30
1950	*	*	£2	£6
1953	*	*	£2	£5
1956	*	*	*	£4
1961	*	*	*	£3
1962	*	*	*	£3
1963	*	*	*	£3
1964	*	*	*	£3
1965	*	*	*	£3
1966	*	*	*	£3
1967	*	*	*	*
1968	*	*	*	*

PENNIES

Year	F	VF	EF	Unc
1928	*	*	£6	£25
1928 proof	*	*	*	£35
1931	*	£2	£25	£80
1933	*	£3	£40	£150
1935	*	*	£15	£45
1937	*	*	£25	£80
1938 (possibly unique)	*	*	*	£37500
1940	*	£15	£145	£600
1941	*	*	£6	£30
1942	*	*	£3	£15
1943	*	*	£5	£20
1946	*	*	£3	£15
1948	*	*	£3	£15
1949	*	*	£3	£15

Year	F	VF	EF	Unc
1950	*	*	£3	£15
1952	*	*	£2	£7
1962	*	*	£2	£3
1963	*	*	*	£2
1964	*	*	*	£2
1965	*	*	*	£1
1966	*	*	*	£1
1967	*	*	*	£1
1968	*	*	*	£1

HALFPENNIES

Year	F	VF	EF	Unc
1928	*	*	£4	£20
1928 proof	*	*	*	£25
1933	*	£20	£100	£450
1935	*	£10	£80	£285
1937	*	*	£12	£40
1939	*	£10	£45	£195
1940	*	£10	£65	£225
1941	*	*	£5	£25
1942	*	*	£2	£20
1943	*	*	£5	£25
1946	*	*	£15	£85
1949	*	*	£3	£18
1953	*	*	*	£4
1964	*	*	*	£2
1965	*	*	*	£2
1966	*	*	*	£2
1967	*	*	*	£1

FARTHINGS

Year	F	VF	EF	Unc
1928	*	*	£3	£12
1928 proof	*	*	*	£20
1930	*	*	£5	£18
1931	£1	£3	£8	£30
1932	£1	£3	£10	£35
1933	*	£2	£5	£25
1935	*	£5	£12	£45
1936	*	£6	£15	£50
1937	*	£2	£5	£20
1939	*	*	£3	£12
1940	*	£3	£6	£35
1941	*	*	£3	£7
1943	*	*	£3	£7
1944	*	*	£3	£7
1946	*	*	£3	£7
1949	*	*	£5	£10
1953	*	*	£3	£7
1959	*	*	£1	£4
1966	*	*	£2	£6

DECIMAL COINAGE

50p, 10p, 5p, 2p, 1p, ½p, all face value only.

SETS

	F	VF	EF	Unc
1928 in card case	*	*	FDC	£325
1928 in leather case	*	*	FDC	£450
1966 unc set	*	*	*	£10
1971 specimen set in folder	*	*	*	£5
1971 proof set	*	*	*	£9

THE ANGLO–GALLIC SERIES

Anyone interested in studying this series should obtain *The Anglo–Gallic Coins* by E R D Elias, who neatly summarised the series: 'All Kings of England in the period 1154–1453 had interests in France. They were Dukes or Lords of Aquitaine, Counts of Poitou or Ponthieu, Lords of Issoudun or they were even or pretended to be, Kings of France itself, and, in those various capacities, struck coins.

These coins, together with the French coins of their sons, and of their English vassals, are called Anglo–Gallic coins'.

See our table for the English kings' French titles.

KINGS OF ENGLAND AND FRANCE 1154–1453	
ENGLAND	FRANCE
Henry II 1154–89 Duke of Normandy and Count of Anjou, Maine and Touraine. By marrying Eleanor of Aquitaine in 1152, he became Duke of Aquitaine and Count of Poitou. He relinquished Aquitaine and Poitou to his son Richard in 1168. In 1185 he forced Richard to surrender Aquitaine and Poitou to Eleanor who governed between 1199–1204.	**Louis VII 1137–80** **Philip II 1180–1223**
Richard I the Lionheart 1189–99 Formally installed as Duke of Aquitaine and Count of Poitou in 1172.	
John 1199–1216 He lost all parts of the Angevin Empire except Aquitaine and part of Poitou.	
Henry III 1216–72 In 1252 he ceded Aquitaine to his son Edward.	**Louis VIII 1223–26** **Louis IX 1226–70** **Philip III 1270–85**
Edward I 1272–1307 He governed Aquitaine from 1252. In 1279 he became Count of Ponthieu. In 1290 the county went to his son Edward.	**Philip IV 1285–1314**
Edward II 1307–27 He was Count of Ponthieu from 1290. In 1325 he relinquished the county of Ponthieu and the Duchy of Aquitaine to his son Edward.	**Louis X 1314–16** **Philip V 1316–22** **Charles IV 1322–28**
Edward III 1327–77 Count of Ponthieu and Duke of Aquitaine from 1325. He lost Ponthieu in 1337 but it was restored in 1360. In 1340 he assumed the title of King of France, which he abandoned again in 1360. He gave Aquitaine to his son, Edward the Black Prince, (b1330–d1376), who was Prince of Aquitaine 1362–1372, although he actually ruled from 1363–1371. In 1369 Edward III reassumed the title King of France.	**Philip VI 1328–50** **John II 1350–64** **Charles V 1364–80**
Richard II 1377–99 The son of the Black Prince succeeded his grandfather, Edward III, as King of England and Lord of Aquitaine.	**Charles VI 1380–1422**
Henry IV 1399–1413 He adopted the same titles as Richard II.	
Henry V 1413–22 From 1417–1420 he used the title King of the French on his 'Royal' French coins. After the Treaty of Troyes in 1420 he styled himself 'heir of France'.	
Henry VI 1422–61 He inherited the title King of the French from his grandfather Charles VI. He lost actual rule in Northern France in 1450 and in Aquitaine in 1453.	**Charles VII 1422–61**

	F	VF
HENRY II 1152–68		
Denier	£50	£120
Obole	£90	£220
RICHARD THE LIONHEART 1168–99		
Aquitaine		
Denier	£60	£140
Obole	£60	£140
Poitou		
Denier	£45	£100
Obole	£60	£160
Issoudun		
Denier	£295	*
ELEANOR 1199–1204		
Denier	£65	£145
Obole	£350	*
EDWARD I		
During the lifetime of his father 1252–72		
Denier au lion	£35	£100
Obole au lion	£45	£125
After succession to the English throne 1272–1307		
Denier au lion	£60	£150
Obole au lion	£165	*
Denier à la croix longue	£70	£165
Au léopard, first type	£35	£90
Obole au léopard, first type	£55	£140
Denier à la couronne	£280	*
EDWARD II		
Gros Turonus Regem	ext. rare	
Maille blanche	ext. rare	
Hibernie	£45	£135
EDWARD III		
Gold coins		
Ecu d'or	£2850	£7250
Florin	£6250	£13000
Léopard d'or, 1st issue	ext. rare	
2nd issue	£4500	£9000
3rd issue	£3250	£7000

	F	VF
4th issue	£3250	£7950
Guyennois d'or, 1st type	£7750	*
2nd type	£5250	£11750
3rd type	£3950	£7000
Silver coins		
Gros aquitainique au léopard	£195	£585
Tournois à la croix mi-longue	£350	£900
À la croix longue	£140	£300
Sterling	£90	£260
Demi-sterling	£165	£450
Gros au léopard passant	£600	*
À la couronne	£160	£425
Au châtel aquitainique	£195	£600
Tournois au léopard au-dessus	£85	£260
À la porte	£85	£260
Aquitainique au léopard au-dessous	£275	*
Blanc au léopard sous couronne	£75	£175
Gros au léopard sous couronne	£210	£600
À la couronne avec léopard	£175	£485
Sterling à la tête barbue	£325	£875
Petit gros de Bordeaux	ext. rare	
Gros au lion	£150	£425
Demi-gros au lion	£295	*
Guyennois of argent (sterling)	£95	£250
Gros au buste	£1250	*
Demi-gros au buste	£585	£1500
Black coins		
Double à la couronne, 1st type	£110	*
2nd type	£90	£265
3rd type	£200	*
Double au léopard	£70	£175
Sous couronne	£35	£100
Guyennois	ext. rare	
Denier au léopard, 2nd type	£35	£100
Obole au léopard, 2nd type	ext. rare	
Denier au léopard, 3rd type	£40	£120
4th type	£35	£100
Obole au léopard, 4th type	£40	£120
Denier au lion	£45	£145

Some issues of the 2nd and 3rd type deniers au léopard are very rare to extremely rare and therefore much more valuable.

EDWARD THE BLACK PRINCE 1362–72

ABOVE: Edward III 2nd issue léopard d'or

ABOVE: Edward the Black Prince chaise d'or of Bordeaux

Gold coins	F	VF
Léopard d'or	£3500	£8750
Guyennois d'or	£3500	£7500
Chaise d'or	£4000	£8500
Pavillon d'or 1st issue	£3950	£8750
2nd issue	£3950	£8750
Demi-pavillon d'or	*	*
Hardi d'or	£4000	£8750

Silver coins		
Gros	£875	£1925
Demi-gros	£110	£300
Sterling	£75	£165
Hardi d'argent	£50	£135

Black coins		
Double guyennois	£120	£295
Denier au lion	£55	£145
Denier	£60	£150

RICHARD II 1377–99

Gold coins		
Hardi d'or	£5500	£11000
Demi-hardi d'or		ext. rare

Silver coins		
Double hardi d'argent	£975	£2850
Hardi d'argent	£55	£165

Black coins		
Denier	£90	£260

HENRY IV 1399–1413

Silver coins		
Double hardi d'argent	£600	£1725
Hardi d'argent	£40	£125
Hardi aux genêts	£185	£575

Black coins		
Denier	£55	£150
Aux genêts	£150	£385

HENRY V 1413–22

Gold coins		
Agnel d'or	£7500	£16500
Salut d'or	£8750	£19750

Silver coins		
Florette, 1st issue	£90	£225
2nd issue	£165	£395
3rd issue	£65	£175
4th issue	£90	£225
Guénar	£425	£985
Gros au léopard	£500	*

Black coins		
Mansiois		ext. rare
Niquet	£60	£180
Denier tournois	£75	£195

HENRY VI 1422–53

Gold coins	F	VF
Salut d'or	£750	£1650
Angelot	£3250	£7500

ABOVE: Henry VI Salut d'or Paris mint

Silver coins		
Grand blanc aux ècus	£75	£225
Petit blanc	£95	£275
Trésin		ext. rare

Black coins		
Denier Paris, 1st issue	£70	£160
2nd issue	£70	£160
Denier tournois	£75	£175
Maille tournois	£75	£175

The prices of the saluts and grands blancs are for mints of Paris, Rouen and Saint Lô; coins of other mints are rare to very rare.

◼ PONTHIEU

EDWARD I		
Denier	£95	£250
Obole	£85	£215

EDWARD III		
Denier	£180	*
Obole	£265	*

◼ BERGERAC

HENRY, EARL OF LANCASTER 1347–51		
Gros tournois à la croix longue	£925	£1950
À la couronne	£825	*
Au châtel aquitainique	£925	£1950
Tournois au léopard au-dessus	£600	£1375
À la couronne		ext. rare
À fleur-de-lis		ext. rare
Au léopard passant		ext. rare
Double	£1350	*
Denier au léopard	£825	*

HENRY, DUKE OF LANCASTER 1351–61		
Gros tournois à la couronne avec léopard	£975	*
Au léopard couchant	£975	*
Sterling à la tête barbue	£825	*
Gros au lion		ext. rare

ISLAND COINAGE

Proofs have been struck for a large number of Channel Islands coins, particularly in the case of Jersey. Except for those included in modern proof sets, most are very rare and in the majority of cases have been omitted from the list.

For further information refer to *The Coins of the British Commonwealth of Nations, Part I, European Territories* by F Pridmore (Spink, 1960). BU prices are for coins with brilliant mint lustre.

■ GUERNSEY

	F	VF	EF	BU
TEN SHILLINGS				
1966	*	*	*	£2.50
THREEPENCE				
1956	*	*	*	£2.50
1959	*	*	*	£2.50
1966 proof	*	*	*	£2.50
EIGHT DOUBLES				
1834	*	£14	£75	£500
1858	*	£14	£75	£400
1864	*	£20	£85	*
1868	*	£15	£70	£195
1874	*	£15	£70	£189
1885 H	*	*	£20	£95
1889 H	*	*	£20	£80
1893 H	*	*	£20	£80
1902 H	*	*	£18	£50
1903 H	*	*	£20	£60
1910 H	*	*	£20	£60
1911 H	*	£20	£50	£120
1914 H	*	*	£15	£50
1918 H	*	*	£15	£50
1920 H	*	*	£8	£30
1934 H	*	*	£8	£30
1934 H 'burnished flan'	*	*	*	£450
1938 H	*	*	*	£15
1945 H	*	*	*	£10
1947 H	*	*	*	£10
1949 H	*	*	*	£10
1956	*	*	*	£7
1956 proof	*	*	*	£10
1959	*	*	*	£3
1966 proof	*	*	*	£3
FOUR DOUBLES				
1830	*	*	£55	£350
1858	*	*	£60	£350
1864	*	£8	£70	£350
1868	*	£8	£60	*
1874	*	*	£50	*
1885 H	*	*	£8	£60
1889 H	*	*	£8	£65
1893 H	*	*	£8	£45
1902 H	*	*	£8	£55
1903 H	*	*	£8	£55
1906 H	*	*	£8	£80
1908 H	*	*	£8	£75
1910 H	*	*	£5	£65
1911 H	*	*	£5	£55
1914 H	*	*	£5	£55
1918 H	*	*	£5	£40
1920 H	*	*	*	£35
1945 H	*	*	*	£18
1949 H	*	*	*	£20
1956	*	*	*	£5
1956 proof	*	*	*	£10
1966 proof	*	*	*	£5
TWO DOUBLES				
1858	*	£35	£140	£370
1868	*	£35	£140	£370
1874	*	£30	£135	£350
1885 H	*	*	£12	£35
1889 H	*	*	£12	£35
1899 H	*	*	£12	£35
1902 H	*	*	£12	£35
1903 H	*	*	£12	£30
1906 H	*	*	£12	£30
1908 H	*	*	£12	£30
1911 H	*	*	£18	£50
1914 H	*	*	£18	£50
1917 H	£30	£55	£140	£300
1918 H	*	*	£12	£30
1920 H	*	*	£12	£30
1929 H	*	*	£5	£12
ONE DOUBLE				
1830	*	*	£20	£75
1868	*	£45	£120	£330
1868/30	*	£45	£120	£330
1885 H	*	*	£3	£20
1889 H	*	*	£3	£20
1893 H	*	*	£3	£20
1899 H	*	*	£3	£20
1902 H	*	*	£3	£20
1903 H	*	*	£3	£20
1911 H	*	*	£3	£20
1911 H new type	*	*	£3	£20
1914 H	*	*	£3	£15
1929 H	*	*	£3	£15
1933 H	*	*	£3	£15
1938 H	*	*	£3	£12

SETS

	BU
1956 proof	£65
1966 proof	£15
1971 proof	£10

For coins after 1971 refer to the *Standard Catalogue of World Coins* published by Krause Publications annually.

www.stampmagazine.co.uk

ISLAND COINAGE

■ JERSEY

CROWN	F	VF	EF	BU
1966	*	*	*	£4
1966 proof	*	*	*	£10

¼ OF A SHILLING

	F	VF	EF	BU
1957	*	*	*	£6
1960 proof only	*	*	*	£85
1964	*	*	*	£4
1966	*	*	*	£4

1/12 OF A SHILLING

	F	VF	EF	BU
1877 H	*	*	£18	£120
1881	*	*	£15	£80
1888	*	*	£15	£70
1894	*	*	£12	£70
1909	*	*	£15	£140
1911	*	*	£10	£70
1913	*	*	£10	£70
1923	*	*	£10	£75
1923 new type	*	*	£12	£70
1926	*	*	£12	£60
1931	*	*	£5	£30
1933	*	*	£5	£30
1935	*	*	£5	£30
1937	*	*	*	£18
'1945' (George VI)	*	*	£5	£12
'1945' (Elizabeth II)	*	*	*	£8
1946	*	*	*	£12
1947	*	*	*	£12
1957	*	*	*	£5
1960	*	*	*	£5
1964	*	*	*	£4
1966	*	*	*	£3
1966 proof	*	*	*	£7

The date 1945 on 1/12 shillings commemorates the year of liberation from German occupation. The coins were struck in 1949, 1950, 1952 and 1954.

1/13 OF A SHILLING

	F	VF	EF	BU
1841	*	*	£75	£420
1844	*	*	£75	£420
1851	*	*	£85	£350
1858	*	*	£70	£300
1861	*	*	£70	£300
1865 proof only	*	*	*	£900
1866	*	*	£40	£160
1870	*	*	£40	£160
1871	*	*	£40	£160

1/24 OF A SHILLING

	F	VF	EF	BU
1877 proof only	*	*	*	£400
1877 H	*	*	£20	£110
1888	*	*	£15	£60
1894	*	*	£15	£60
1909	*	*	£15	£75
1911	*	*	£12	£50
1913	*	*	£12	£50

	F	VF	EF	BU
1923	*	*	£10	£50
1923 new type	*	*	£10	£50
1926	*	*	£12	£55
1931	*	*	£7	£25
1933	*	*	£7	£20
1935	*	*	£7	£15
1937	*	*	£7	£12
1946	*	*	£7	£12
1947	*	*	£7	£12

1/26 OF A SHILLING

	F	VF	EF	BU
1841	*	*	£55	£260
1844	*	*	£60	£290
1851	*	*	£55	£260
1858	*	*	£50	£260
1861	*	*	£45	£220
1866	*	*	£25	£175
1870	*	*	£25	£175
1871	*	*	£25	£175

1/48 OF A SHILLING

	F	VF	EF	BU
1877 proof	*	*	*	£400
1877 H	*	£25	£95	£275

1/52 OF A SHILLING

	F	VF	EF	BU
1841	*	£40	£175	£395
1841 proof	*	*	*	£1300
1861 proof	*	*	*	£1400

Decimal coinage

SETS	BU
1957	£40
1960	£15
1964	£12
1966 four coins, proof	£8
1966 two crowns	£10
1972 Silver Wedding five gold, four silver coins	BV
1972 proof	BV
1972 four silver coins	£50

For coins after 1972 refer to the *Standard Catalogue of World Coins* published by Krause Publications annually.

■ ISLE OF MAN

Contemporary forgeries of earlier Isle of Man coins exist.

Copper and Bronze 1709–1839

ABOVE: James Stanley, 10th Earl of Derby, penny, 1709

PENNIES	F	VF	EF	Unc
1709	£50	£120	*	*
1733	£45	£200	£395	*
1733 proof	*	*	£500	*

ABOVE: Proof penny in silver, 1733

	F	VF	EF	Unc
1733 silver	*	£400	£750	£1400
1758	£40	£100	£300	*
1758 proof	*	*	£1000	*
1758 silver	*	*	£2500	*
1786	£15	£50	£200	£485
1786 plain edge proof	*	*	£750	£1600
1798	£15	£60	£250	£600
1798 bronzed proof	*	*	£425	£750
1798 AE gilt proof	*	*	£1250	£2500
1798 silver proof	*	*	£2000	£3000
1813	£15	£60	£250	£600
1813 bronze proof	*	*	£425	£700
1813 gilt proof	*	*	£1250	£2500
1839	*	£15	£75	£275
1839 proof	*	*	*	£1500
1841 proof	*	*	*	£3500
1859 proof	*	*	*	£5000

HALFPENNIES	F	VF	EF	Unc
1709	£75	£185	*	*
1723	£1250	*	*	*
1723 silver	£1500	*	*	*
1733	£50	£125	£275	£500
1733 proof	*	*	£650	£1000
1733 silver	*	*	£900	£1500
1758	£20	£60	£265	*
1758 proof	*	*	*	£2000
1786	£10	£45	£150	£275
1786 plain edge proof	*	*	£425	£875
1798	£10	£40	£100	£265

ABOVE: Proof halfpenny, 1798

	F	VF	EF	Unc
1798 proof	£10	£30	£275	£400
1798 silver proof	*	*	£1650	£3000
1798 gilt proof	*	*	*	£1500
1813	£10	£30	£225	£350
1813 proof	*	*	£250	£600
1813 gilt proof	*	*	*	£1700
1839	*	*	£45	£225
1839 proof	*	*	*	£3000

FARTHINGS	F	VF	EF	Unc
1839	£10	£25	£45	£125
1839 proof	*	*	*	£625
1841 proof only	*	*	*	£1750
1860 proof only	*	*	*	£3500
1864 proof only	*	*	*	£4000

BRITISH PAPER MONEY

As of June 2021 only three out of the four current polymer denominations have been Issued with the Sarah John signature.

Condition is the most important factor in banknote pricing although it's possible to collect an attractive selection in lower grades; some notes are never seen in better than Very Fine.

We have not listed banknotes prior to 1914 as these are scarce and generally only available in grades up to Very Fine.

Serial numbers with the prefix 'No' are referred to as 'dot' if 'No' is followed by a full stop and 'dash' if followed by a dash.

Reference numbers are according to Vincent Duggleby's *English Paper Money*. The 9th edition (Pam West, 2017) is a must for the collector.

■ TREASURY NOTES

		JOHN BRADBURY	VF	EF
		First issue		
T1	£1	Black on white, prefix large letters A, B or C	£1800	£2600
T2	£1	No full stop after serial letter	£2800	£4500
T3	£1	Six digits	£800	£1250
T4	£1	Large serial number, 'dot' and five digits	£900	£1750
T5	£1	Large serial number, 'dash' and five digits	£900	£1600
T6	£1	Letter, letter, number, number	£1100	£1800
T7	£1	Small typeface serial number	rare	
T8	10s	Red on white, six digits	£700	£1200
T9	10s	Prefix 'No'	£520	£820
T10	10s	Red on white, five digits	£950	£1500
		Second issue		
T12	10s	Red on white, five digits	£420	£700
T13	10s	Six digits	£380	£650
T11	£1	Black on white	£380	£700
T14	£1	Arabic overprint	£4500	£9000
T15	10s	Arabic overprint	£820	£1600
		Third issue		
T16	£1	Green and brown on white	£140	£280
T17	10s	Black serial no with 'dot'	£540	£850
T18	10s	Black serial no with 'dash'	£510	£830
T19	10s	Red serial no with 'dot'	£2000	*
T20	10s	Red serial no with 'dash'	£430	£750
		NORMAN FENWICK WARREN FISHER		
		First issue		
T24	£1	Green and brown on white	£80	£170
T25	10s	Green and brown on white, 'dot'	£250	£450
T26	10s	'Dash'	£220	£400
		Second issue		
T30	10s	Green and brown on white	£170	£330
T31	£1	'Dot'	£95	£190
T32	£1	Square 'dot'	£190	£360
		Third issue, Northern Ireland		
T33	10s	Green and brown on white	£210	£480
T34	£1	'Dot'	£120	£210
T35	£1	Square 'dot'	£210	£420
		Fractionals		
T27	5s	Violet and green on white	£8000	£12000
T28	2s 6d	Olive-green and chocolate	£9500	*
T29	1s	Green and brown on white	£9000	*

■ BANK OF ENGLAND NOTES

		CYRIL PATRICK MAHON 1925–29	VF	EF
B210	10s	Red-brown	£130	£270
B212	£1	Green	£130	£250
B215	£5	Black and white	£450	£800
		BASIL GAGE CATTERNS 1929–34		
B223	10s	Red-brown:	£70	£120
B225	£1	Green: letter, number, number	£30	£65
B226	£1	Number, number, letter	£100	£220
B228	£5	Black on white	£300	£500
		KENNETH OSWALD PEPPIATT 1934–49		
B236	10s	Red-brown: number, number, letter 1st period	£35	£70
B238	£1	Green: number, number, letter, 1st issue	£25	£60
B241	£5	Black on white, one straight edge, three deckled	£200	£350
B249	£1	Blue (shades), 2nd issue	£12	£25
B251	10s	Mauve, 2nd period	£35	£70
B255	£5	Straight edges, metal filament, thick paper	£130	£220
B256	10s	Red-brown: number, number, letter, 3rd period	£70	£140
B258	£1	Green: letter, number, number, letter, 3rd issue	£18	£45
B260	£1	Metal filament, 4th issue	£10	£22
B262	10s	Metal filament, 4th period	£30	£70
B264	£5	Straight edges, metal filament, thin paper	£130	£220
		Fractionals		
B253	5s	Olive-green on pale pink background	from £6000	*
B254	2s 6d	Black on pale blue background	from £6000	*
		PERCIVAL SPENCER BEALE 1949–55		
B265	10s	Red-brown: number, number, letter	£18	£35
B266	10s	letter, number, number, letter	£12	£25
B268	£1	Green	£5	£15
B270	£5	Black on white	£110	£160

LESLIE KENNETH O'BRIEN 1955–62

B271	10s	Red-brown: letter, number, number, letter	£6	£15
B272	10s	Replacement	£55	£110
B273	£1	Green	£6	£12
B275	£5	Black on white	£120	£210
B277	£5	Blue, pale green and orange, solid blue symbols reverse	£22	£45
B280	£5	Hollow white £5 symbols reverse	£22	£45

Queen's portrait			EF	Unc
B281	£1	Letter, number, number	£4	£8
B282	£1	Number, number, letter	£4	£8
B284	£1	Letter, number, number, letter	£16	£30

JASPER QUINTUS HOLLOM 1962–66

B288	£1	Green	£4	£8
B292	£1	Green, letter 'G' reverse	£8	£18
B294	10s	Red-brown: number, number, letter	£4	£8
B295	10s	Red-brown: number, number, letter	£4	£8
3B297	£5	Blue	£25	£60
B299	£10	Multicoloured brown	£35	£70

JOHN STANDISH FFORDE 1966–70

B301	£1	Green	£5	£12
B303	£1	'G' variety	£8	£15
B309	10s	Red-brown: number, number, letter	£4	£8
B310	10s	Letter, number, number, letter	£4	£8
B311	10s	Letter, number, number	£8	£14
B312	£5	Blue: letter, number, number	£25	£60
B314	£5	Number, number, letter	£25	£60
B316	£10	Multicoloured brown	£35	£70
B318	£20	Multicoloured purple	£320	£460

JOHN BRANGWYN PAGE 1970–80

B322	£1	Green: letter, letter, number, number	£3	£6
B324	£5	Blue	£30	£65
B326	£10	Multicoloured	£35	£65
B328	£20	Multicoloured purple	£45	£90
B330	£10	Letter, number, number	£25	£45
B332	£5	Multicoloured: letter, number, number, 1st series	£14	£30
B334	£5	L on reverse, signifies lithographic printing	£14	£30

DAVID HENRY FITZROY SOMERSET 1980–88

B341	£1	Green	£3	£6
B343	£5	Multicoloured: letter, letter, number, number	£10	£25
B346	£10	Multicoloured: letter, number, number	£32	£80

B350	£20	Multicoloured purple	£50	£110
B352	£50	Olive green, brown, grey	£85	£140

GEORGE MALCOLM GILL 1988–91

B353	£5	Blue	£10	£25
B354	£10	Brown	£20	£40
B355	£20	Multicoloured purple	£65	£130
B356	£50	Olive green, brown, grey	£120	£250
B357	£5	Turquoise, Series E	£12	£25
B358	£20	Multicoloured purple	£45	£90

GRAHAM EDWARD ALFRED KENTFIELD 1991–1998

B360	£10	Multicoloured brown	£40	£80
B361	£50	Olive green, brown, grey	£95	£180
B362	£5	Turquoise	£20	£45
B363	£5	Multicoloured letter, letter, number, number	£12	£25
B364	£5	Multicoloured blue	£10	£20
B366	£10	Orange brown	£18	£35
B369	£10	Orange brown	£16	£35
B371	£20	Multicoloured purple	£45	£95
B374	£20	Multicoloured purple	£40	£90
B377	£50	Red	£70	£120

MERLYN VIVIENNE LOWTHER 1999–2004

B380	£5	Turquoise	£10	£20
B382	£10	Orange brown	£25	£45
B384	£20	Multicoloured purple	£60	£100
B385	£50	Red	£70	£120
B386	£20	Multicoloured purple	£25	£40
B388	£10	Orange And 'Co'	£16	£32
B390	£10	Orange The 'Co'	£16	£30
B393	£5	Turquoise	£8	£18
B395	£5	Turquoise	£8	£15

ANDREW JOHN BAILEY 2004–2011

B398	£5	Turquoise	£8	£15
B400	£10	Orange brown	£12	£18
B402	£20	Purple	£25	£40
B404	£50	Red	£70	£110
B405	£20	Purple, Adam Smith reverse	£25	£35

CHRIS SALMON 2011–2014

B407	£5	Turquoise	£6	£10
B408	£10	Orange brown	£12	£20
B409	£20	Purple	£25	£35
B410	£50	Red, Boulton, Watt reverse	£55	£85

VICTORIA CLELAND 2014– 2018

B411	£10	Orange brown	£12	£18
B412	£20	Purple	£28	£40
B413	£50	Red, Boulton, Watt reverse	£60	£75
B414	£5	Polymer, Churchill		£8
B415	£10	Polymer, Jane Austen		£14

No paper £5 notes were issued with Cleland signature

SARAH JOHN 2018–

B416	£20	Polymer, Turner	face	£8
B417	£10	Polymer, Jane Austen	face	£14
B418	£50	Polymer, Alan Turing	face	£65

ADVERTISING INDEX